HOW TO MAKE
ALIGNMENT CHARTS

HOW TO MAKE ALIGNMENT CHARTS

BY

MERRILL G. VAN VOORHIS, M.Sc.

FIRST EDITION
SECOND IMPRESSION

McGRAW-HILL BOOK COMPANY, Inc.

NEW YORK AND LONDON

1937

THE MAPLE PRESS COMPANY, YORK, PA.

PREFACE

It is the purpose of this volume to provide the most direct instructions on how to make nomographic or alignment charts for the solution of engineering and other formulas. Major stress is placed on how to handle the various types of equations. Theory of construction, which is not essential to the understanding of the procedure in making the charts, is not interspersed with the material, but is briefly outlined in the Appendix for reference. Graphical construction methods are described wherever they are practical, along with a mathematical method.

The material is presented with a minimum of text and a maximum of illustrations. Examples are given with every type equation to demonstrate the detailed procedure for making the charts according to the directions that are provided. The first formulas treated are of the simplest type. As groups of equations are described, their relations to each other and to certain general type forms become obvious. By this plan of presentation, the material is gathered together to build a theory as contrasted with presentations wherein an all-inclusive theory is traced to its many branches.

Alignment charts, although by no means a new method for solving equations graphically, are being appreciated more fully. Although it may seem that one more text on this subject is superfluous in view of the wealth of material that has been written, it has been the experience of the author in presenting a course of nomography to technical men that there is need for a more direct approach to the subject. The aim is therefore to make the procedure as recipe-like as possible so that knowledge of theory is not essential.

In general there are two theoretical approaches to the subject —by plane and analytical geometry and by determinants. The author favors the former and uses it here chiefly because determinants are a relatively unfamiliar branch of mathematics.

In drawing up the material for this text the writer has profited from several sources, modifying it to suit the requirements

found while giving a course of instruction.   Those sources which
have been particularly valuable in outlining this course and in
preparing this text are evenly divided as to manner of approach:
"A First Course in Nomography," by S. Brodetsky (Open Port
Publishing Co., Chicago, Ill.); "Graphical and Mechanical Com-
putation, Part I, Alignment Charts," by Joseph Lipka (John
Wiley & Sons, Inc., New York); "Design of Diagrams for
Engineering Formulas," by Laurence I. Hewes and Herbert L.
Seward (McGraw-Hill Book Company, Inc., New York); and
"The Nomogram," by H. J. Allcock and J. Reginald Jones
(Pitman Publishing Co., New York).

   Although the author has not had access to the work of d'Ocagne,
who, over fifty years ago, developed the principles of alignment
charts and published them under the title "Traité de nomo-
graphie," acknowledgment is due him for opening this field of
practical mathematics.

                                      MERRILL G. VAN VOORHIS.

   CLEVELAND, OHIO,
      July, 1937.

CONTENTS

CONTENTS

LIST OF GENERAL TYPE EQUATIONS

Although the symbol for the function of the variable is omitted in the following list, it is to be understood that any other more complex function of a given variable may be substituted for the simple variable (see page 7, first paragraph under Type 4).

	Types	Pages	Figures
$X + Y = Z$	1, 3, 4	1, 5, 7	1–4, 6
$X - Y = Z$	2, 3, 4	4, 5, 7	5
$X \pm Y \pm U \pm$ $V \pm \cdots = Z$	9	24	
$X \pm Y = U \pm V$	12	41	28
$XY = Z$	5, 7, 8	11, 15, 18	7, 8, 9, 11, 12, 13
$XY = UV$	9, 13	24, 44	15, 16
$\dfrac{X}{Y} = Z$	6, 7, 8, 10	15, 18, 29	9, 10, 12, 14, 19, 21, 22
$XYUV = Z$	9	24	
$\dfrac{X}{Y} = \dfrac{U}{V}$	9, 11, 13 16	24, 38, 44, 52	16, 17, 18, 26, 27, 30, 31, 32, 39
$XY = U \pm V$		33, 36	23, 25 (Key I)
$\dfrac{X}{Y} = U \pm V$	14	46	24, 33, 34, 35
$\dfrac{X + Y}{X - Y} = UV = \dfrac{U}{1/V}$	15	50	37
$\dfrac{X + Y}{X - Y} = \dfrac{U}{V}$	15	50	37
$\dfrac{XY}{X \pm Y} = Z$	17	54	6, 40, 41
$\dfrac{1}{X} + \dfrac{1}{Y} = \dfrac{1}{Z}$	17	54	6, 40, 41
$\dfrac{X}{Y(X + Y)} = Z$ $\left(\text{May be written } \dfrac{1/Y}{Z} + \dfrac{Y}{X} = 1\right)$	19	73	
$X_1 \pm X_2 Y = Z$	18	56	43–51, 57–60
$\dfrac{X_1}{Y} \pm \dfrac{X_2}{Z} = 1$	19	73	52–56, 61

LIST OF FORMULAS CHARTED

xi

HOW TO MAKE
ALIGNMENT CHARTS

HOW TO MAKE ALIGNMENT CHARTS

TYPE 1

The simplest equation that can be written is that for the sum of two simple variables. The determination of the sum by the usual method is so simple that it would be impractical to construct a chart for the solution of the equation. But the directions are given here because they present the fundamentals and afford a comparison with the directions given later for the construction of charts for more complex equations.

Nomogram for $x + y = z$

Draw two parallel lines for the x and y scales, as in Fig. 1.

Determine for the particular equation to be charted the maximum and minimum values of x and y, respectively, that are to be included in the chart.

Subdivide one line uniformly with a scale for x within the limits established and subdivide the other line similarly for y, the two scales ascending in the same direction. The size of each scale is independent of the other and may be as large as the space allows.

Under these conditions of layout the location of the z scale, as shown in Fig. 1, will always be a line parallel with and between the x and y scale lines. Two methods may be employed to find the location of this line, a construction method and a formula method.

CONSTRUCTION METHOD FOR LOCATING z SCALE

Select a value for z within the range of its scale and determine two sets of values of x and y yielding the selected value of z in the equation. Draw two lines connecting the corresponding values of x and y on their respective scales. The intersection of these two lines locates the z scale line, and also the selected value of z in the z scale.   Repeat this operation to obtain a

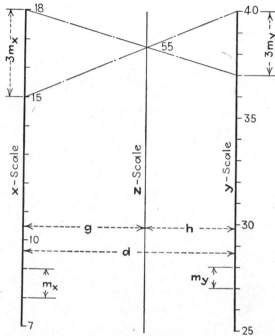

Fig. 1.—Nomogram for determining the sum of two simple variables.   Construction of this simple chart presents the fundamentals for charts for more complex equations.

second value of z in the scale and subdivide the z scale uniformly (see Appendix 1).

Formula Method for Locating z Scale

To determine the distances between scale lines by formulas, it can be shown by similar triangles, as in Fig. 2, that

$$g = \frac{m_x}{m_x + m_y}d \qquad (1)$$

$$h = \frac{m_y}{m_x + m_y}d \text{ (see Appendix 2)} \qquad (2)$$

g = distance from z scale to x scale.
h = distance from z scale to y scale.
d = distance between x and y scales = $g + h$.
m = length of scale unit for the scale designated by subscript.

Laying out these distances and scale values, as indicated in Fig. 1, gives the desired construction.

The size of the z scale unit, m_z, can be determined also by either a construction method or a formula method.

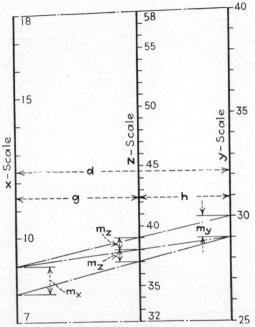

FIG. 2.—Determination of the size of the z scale units by the construction method and demonstrating the proof of the formula.

CONSTRUCTION METHOD FOR DETERMINING SIZE OF z SCALE UNIT

Draw a line crossing the upper end values of the x and y scales and another crossing the lower end values of the x and y scales. The corresponding values of z for the top and bottom of the z scale can then be determined from the equation $x + y = z$. This gives the numerical values at the top and at the bottom of the z scale. Subdivide the z scale uniformly between the upper and lower z scale values.

FORMULA METHOD FOR DETERMINING SIZE OF z SCALE UNIT

Referring to Fig. 2, from similar triangles,

$$m_z = \frac{h}{d}m_x = \frac{g}{d}m_y = \frac{m_x m_y}{m_x + m_y}$$

Solving this equation with the known values of m_x and m_y, as used on the x and y scales, respectively, the z scale can be laid out. The starting point can be readily obtained, as shown in Fig. 1 and described previously.

TYPE 2

Nomogram for $x - y = z$

The same procedure is followed for the equation $x - y = z$, as charted in Fig. 3, as was followed for the equation $x + y = z$,

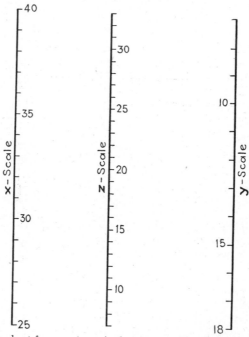

FIG. 3.—The chart for $x - y = z$ is the same as the one for $x + y = z$, except that the x and y scales ascend in opposite directions, with the x and z scales in the same direction.

Fig. 1, with the exception that the x and y scales ascend in opposite directions. The z scale ascends in the same direction as the x scale.

ILLUSTRATIVE EXAMPLES

In most of the examples given, the distance between divisions on the scales is greater than would normally be required for a chart designed for use.   The object here is to show many simple figures rather than a few with great detail.

To illustrate the construction of a chart for the equation $x + y = z$ with an actual example, assume the following ranges: $x = 7$ to 18 and $y = 25$ to 40.   The limits of z will then be 32 to 58, as determined from the relationship $x + y = z$.   In Fig. 1, the equally divided x scale of 11 divisions and the y scale of 15 divisions are laid out on parallel lines, taking most advantage of the available space.   Any value of z can be used to locate the z scale by construction.   In Fig. 1, a value of $z = 55$ was selected. Among the numerous values of x and y that will satisfy the equations are $x = 18$ and $y = 37$, and $y = 40$ and $x = 15$.   Two intersecting lines through these values of x and y locate 55 $(18 + 37 = 55 = 40 + 15)$ on the z scale, and a line is then drawn through the intersection parallel to the x and y scale lines.

On the original nomogram from which Fig. 1 was reduced, it was determined by measurement that $m_x = 0.806$ in., $m_y = 0.594$ in., and $d = 5.90$ in.   With these figures and using formula (1),

$$g = \frac{m_x}{m_x + m_y} d = \frac{0.806 \times 5.90}{0.806 + 0.594} = 3.40 \text{ in.}$$

Measurements made over 10 subdivisions on each scale increase the accuracy of the determination.

Since z varies through a range of 26 units, 26 uniform divisions are placed on the z scale between the limiting lines drawn from $x = 18$ to $y = 40$ and from $x = 7$ to $y = 25$, as shown in Fig. 2. Or the length of these divisions can be determined by the formula

$$m_z = \frac{m_x \times m_y}{m_x + m_y} = \frac{0.806 \times 0.594}{0.806 + 0.594} = 0.3425$$

As stated above, the letter m can represent multiples of 10 or more units, as well as a single unit, with resulting increased accuracy.

TYPE 3

Nomogram for $ax \pm by = cz$

The constants a, b, and c may be ignored if the construction method is used.   The procedure is then identical with that for the types $x \pm y = z$.

In the formula method, modifications allow for the constants. For the location of the z scale line by the formula method,

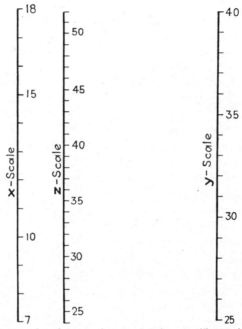

FIG. 4.—Nomogram for the equation $2x + 0.4y = z$, illustrating the method used for the type equation $ax + by = cz$.

it can be shown by similar triangles, using the same method as shown in Fig. 2, that

$$\frac{g}{d} = \frac{\dfrac{m_x}{a}}{\dfrac{m_x}{a} + \dfrac{m_y}{b}}$$

Then the size of the z scale unit will be

$$\frac{m_z}{c} = \frac{hm_x}{da} = \frac{gm_y}{db} = \frac{\left(\dfrac{m_x}{a}\right)\left(\dfrac{m_y}{b}\right)}{\dfrac{m_x}{a} + \dfrac{m_y}{b}} = \frac{m_x m_y}{bm_x + am_y}$$

It is observed that the constant always accompanies the same variable that it does in the type equation. In other respects the formulas for location and size of the z scale are identical with those for the equation $x + y = z$, as described above (see Appendix 3).

The procedure may be checked readily in Fig. 4, which is a nomogram for the equation $2x + 0.4y = z$, where the ranges of x and y are the same as in the previous examples.

TYPE 4

Nomogram for $f_1(x) \pm f_2(y) = f_3(z)$

Throughout the remainder of this book the above symbols will be used to indicate functions of a variable. The use of functions enables simplifications of formulas that would otherwise appear impossible to put into nomographic form. A function of x is commonly written $f(x)$. Where different functions are used together, a subscript is used to differentiate between them; thus, $f_2(x)$ is not the same as $f_3(x)$, but $f_2(x)$ and $f_2(y)$ indicate the same function of y as of x.

A function of x contains the one variable, x, but can be combined with any number of constants. Some examples of functions of x are x^2, $\log x$, $ax + b$, $x^2 + x - 5$, and even

$$\cos^{-1}(1 - x) - (1 - x)\sqrt{2x - x^2}$$

The equations discussed thus far, illustrating the different types, have been special instances of the above function equation. The scale of the variable can now assume unlimited form, but the function scales remain uniformly divided. For example, if $f(x) = \log x$, the scale would be the familiar logarithmic scale; if $f(x) = x^2$, the scale of x would be determined in the following manner:

Assuming that the limits of x are 0 and 10, $f(x)$ will vary from 0 to 100 and the $f(x)$ scale will be uniform over this range. Values of x from 1 to 10 would be placed opposite function values of 0, 1, 4, 9, 16, and up to 100.

It is obvious that the procedure of making a nomogram of function scales is identical in every respect with the procedure for the simple formula $x \pm y = z$. The replacement of function scales with scales of the variable, as indicated in the preceding paragraph, is the only additional step necessary to complete the nomogram.

The following example, illustrated in Fig. 5, will clarify the procedure. The strength factor for bevel gears is often determined by the empirical formula

$$S = \frac{FY'}{P}\left(1 - M + \frac{M^2}{3}\right)$$

in which M is a factor depending upon the relative number of teeth in the mating gears and two other factors, and F, Y', and P are all variables which, for the sake of simplicity, will be treated as a single variable X. The equation then can be written

$$\log S = \log X + \log\left(1 - M + \frac{M^2}{3}\right)$$

Let the limits of S be 0.1 to 0.65 and of M be 0.05 to 1.3. The limits of X are 0.1 to 2.5. From these limits, the limits of the functions can be determined easily from a table of logarithms.

Log S varies from $9.00 - 10$ to $9.813 - 10$; $\log\left(1 - M + \frac{M^2}{3}\right)$

varies from $9.978 - 10$ to $9.420 - 10$; and $\log X$ varies between the limits of $9.000 - 10$ and 0.398. Rewriting the equation in the following order:

$$\log S - \log\left(1 - M + \frac{M^2}{3}\right) = \log X$$

puts it into the standard form for placing the X scale between the other two scales.

If uniformly divided scales of the functions of S and M are laid out, as indicated in the procedure for the equation $x - y = z$, the result will be as indicated by the scales on the left side of the lines in Fig. 5. The location of the scale line for X might be determined by selecting the value of $f(X) = \log X = 0$. Then, when $f(S) = 9.800 - 10$, $f(M) = 9.800 - 10$ and, when

$$f(S) = 9.500 - 10, \; f(M) = 9.500 - 10.$$

Two intersecting lines through these values of $f(S)$ and $f(M)$ locate 0 on the $f(X)$ scale, and the latter scale line is then drawn through the intersection parallel to the two scale lines already drawn. In checking the formula method it is to be observed that the $f(M)$ scale has finer divisions than the $f(S)$ scale. Measurements over a group of fine subdivisions should be made, for example, from 9.48 to 9.98 for the $f(M)$ scale and from 9.0 to 9.5 for the $f(S)$ scale to increase accuracy.

The size of the scale units of the $f(X)$ scale is dependent upon the size of the other two function-scale units and the scale is

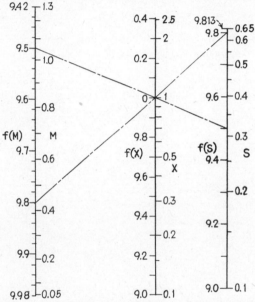

Fig. 5.—Illustrating the procedure for making an alignment chart for the equation of the strength factor S for bevel gears.

laid out in the same manner as the z scale previously described. At this stage there are three uniformly divided scales of the functions which are shown on the left sides of the three scale lines. The replacement of these scales with scales of S, X, and M is the final step. A three-place logarithmic table is all that is necessary in subdividing the strength factor and x scales, but a calculation is required for every point or division line made on the M scale. It is convenient to prepare a table of the division values desired on the unknown scale and the computed values of the function. The following table shows such values:

M	$f(M)$	M	$f(M)$
0.1	$9.956 - 10$	0.7	$9.666 - 10$
0.2	9.910	0.8	9.616
0.3	9.863	0.9	9.568
0.4	9.815	1.0	9.523
0.5	9.766	1.1	9.482
0.6	9.716	1.2	9.447
		1.3	9.420

Normally, the completed nomogram will have only the scale subdivisions shown in Fig. 5 on the right sides of the lines.

Another example which works out a little simpler is the equation for determining the resistance of a pair of parallel resistances:

$$\frac{1}{r_1} + \frac{1}{r_2} = \frac{1}{R}$$

The function equation is simply

$$f(r_1) + f(r_2) = f(R)$$

(No subscripts are used on the symbol f since the functions are similar.)   Let the limits of r_1 be 10 to 15 ohms and of r_2, 40 to 50 ohms.   The limits of the reciprocals or functions will be, for r_1, 0.1 to 0.0667 and, for r_2, 0.025 to 0.02.   These values will give $f(R)$ the limits of 0.0867 to 0.125.

Uniformly divided scales of the functions of r_1 and r_2 are shown on the left side of lines in Fig. 6.   The location of the scale line for R is determined in Fig. 6 by using the following substitutions in the above function equation:

$$0.086 + 0.025 = 0.111 = 0.09 + 0.021.$$

Lines through these values of $f(r_1)$ and $f(r_2)$ locate 0.111 on the $f(R)$ scale line, which is then drawn through the intersection parallel to the two scale lines already drawn.

Drawing of this line is followed by placement of the $f(R)$ scale on the line.   The nomogram is then ready for replacement of function scales with scales of the variables.   In this case the easiest procedure is to reproduce the scales from a table of reciprocals given in many handbooks. If such tables are not available, it will be necessary, as before, to prepare a table by computation of the desired values for the scale divisions, only a few of which are shown in Fig. 6

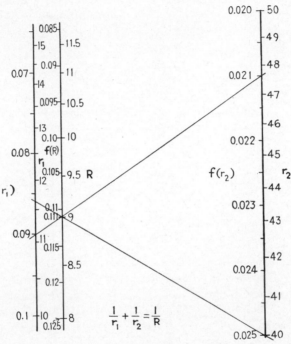

$$\frac{1}{r_1} + \frac{1}{r_2} = \frac{1}{R}$$

Fig. 6.—The equation for electrical resistance of parallel conductors is handled as an equation of Type 4, the sum of two functions.

TYPE 5

Graphic solutions of equations containing multiplication and division of variables and functions of variables are most frequently desired. The construction methods that follow for Figs. 7 and 8 are similar in phrasing to those which have been given for Figs. 1 to 4. The principal difference is the short cut of direct application of logarithmic scales. Reproduction of logarithmic scales is facilitated by the use of standard logarithmic scales, which are available in many sizes on logarithmic graph paper. Such scales may be traced or projected to the same size or to smaller sizes.

Nomogram for $xy = z$

Draw two parallel lines for the x and y scales, as in Fig. 7. Determine for the particular equation to be charted the maximum and minimum values of x and y, respectively, that are to be included in the chart. Subdivide one line with a logarithmic scale for x within the limits given and the other line similarly

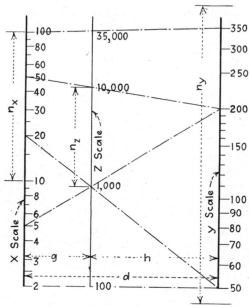

Fig. 7.—Nomogram for $xy = z$ using logarithmic scales. The scale sizes are independent of each other.

for y, the two scales ascending in the same direction. The size of each scale is independent of the other and can be as large as the space allows for the given limits. The z scale will always be on a line parallel with and between the x and y scale lines under the above conditions of layout.

CONSTRUCTION METHOD FOR LOCATING THE z SCALE LINE

Select a value of z within the range of its scale and determine two sets of values of x and y yielding the selected value of z in the equation. Draw two lines connecting the corresponding determined values of x and y on their respective scales. The intersection of these two lines locates the z scale line, and also the selected value of z upon the z scale line.

FORMULA METHOD FOR DETERMINING DISTANCES BETWEEN SCALE LINES IN TERMS OF LOGARITHMIC-CYCLE LENGTHS

$$g = \frac{n_x}{n_x + n_y}d$$

$$h = \frac{n_y}{n_x + n_y}d$$

g = distance from z scale to x scale.
h = distance from z scale to y scale.
d = distance between x and y scales = $g + h$.
n = length of logarithmic cycles designated by subscript.

Laying out these distances and scale values as indicated in Fig. 7 gives the desired construction.

CONSTRUCTION METHOD TO GET THE SIZE OF z SCALE

Draw lines connecting the upper values of the x and y scales and between the lower ends of these scales. The corresponding values of z for the top and bottom of the z scale can then be determined from the equation $xy = z$. The z scale is subdivided logarithmically between these two z values.

FORMULA METHOD TO GET THE SIZE OF z SCALE LOGARITHMIC CYCLE, n_z

$$n_z = \frac{h}{d}n_x = \frac{h}{d}n_y = \frac{n_x n_y}{n_x + n_y}$$

A starting point on the z scale can be determined by selecting a value of z within its range and determining values of x and y that will yield this value of z in the equation. A line drawn across the three scales at the determined values of x and y will locate the selected value of z on the z scale.

Assuming the following ranges in the equation $xy = z$, which is charted in Fig. 8, $x = 7$ to 18 and $y = 25$ to 40. Then z may vary from 175 to 720. The logarithmic scales for x and y are laid out on parallel lines taking most advantage of the available space.

To locate the z scale line by the construction method, any value of z could be used. If $z = 300$ is chosen, $x = 12$ when $y = 25$; and $x = 7.5$ when $y = 40$; therefore, $12 \times 25 = 300 = 7.5 \times 40$.

Two intersecting lines through these values of x and y locate 300 on the z scale, and a line is then drawn through the intersection parallel to the x and y scale lines.

If the nomogram were drawn on 8½- by 11-in. paper, the length of the x scale cycle could be 25 in. since only approximately 0.4 of the cycle length is used. This may be readily checked on an ordinary 10-in. slide rule; the distance from 7 to 10

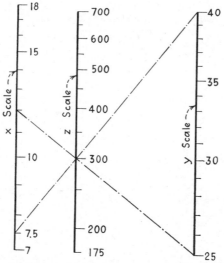

Fig. 8.—The chart for the equation $xy = z$ can also be applied to a transposition of this formula, namely $z/y = x$ or $z/x = y$.

is roughly 1½ in. and from 10 to 18 is roughly 2½ in., making a total of 4 in. of the 10-in. length. The length of the y cycle could be 50 in. since only 0.2 of the cycle length is used. Unless logarithmic scales of these lengths or longer are available for transferring or projecting the scale, a table of logarithms can be used in producing the scale on a uniformly divided scale of appropriate size (or on cross-section paper if the completed chart is to be traced for reproduction).

Assuming 25- and 50-in. cycles are used, $n_x = 25$ and $n_y = 50$. Then $g = \dfrac{25d}{25 + 50} = \dfrac{d}{3}$; thus $g = 2.333$ in. when $d = 7$ in. The length of the z scale cycle as determined by formula is

$$n_z = \frac{25 \times 50}{25 + 50} = 16.667 \text{ in.} = \frac{n_y}{3} = \frac{2n_x}{3}$$

TYPE 6
Nomogram for $x/y = z$

It is evident that the nomogram for $xy = z$ is the same as for $z/y = x$ or $z/x = y$. Therefore the nomogram shown in Fig. 8 can be applied to any of these three equations. But to follow a conventional plan of placing the z scale between the x and y scales in the equation $x/y = z$, the same procedure as for the equation $xy = z$ is employed with the exception that x and y scales ascend in opposite directions. The z scale ascends in the same direction as the x scale.

TYPE 7
Nomogram for $x^a y^b = z^c$ and $x^a/y^b = z^c$

The constants a, b, and c may be ignored if the construction method is used, and the process is identical with that for the equations $xy = z$ and $x/y = z$. The variations in the formulas allow for the constants. (Compare with those for $ax \pm by = cz$.)

The location of the z scale is

$$\frac{g}{d} = \frac{\dfrac{n_x}{a}}{\dfrac{n_x}{a} + \dfrac{n_y}{b}}$$

The size of the z scale logarithmic cycle is

$$\frac{n_z}{c} = \frac{hn_x}{da} = \frac{gn_y}{db} = \frac{\left(\dfrac{n_x}{a}\right)\left(\dfrac{n_y}{b}\right)}{\dfrac{n_x}{a} + \dfrac{n_y}{b}} = \frac{n_x n_y}{bn_x + an_y}$$

The formula for determining the volume of liquid in a vertical cylindrical tank can be used to illustrate. The equation is

$$V = 0.25\pi D^2 H$$

V = volume.
D = diameter.
H = height of the liquid in the tank.

If linear measurements are in feet and volume measurements are in gallons, the formula becomes

$$V = \frac{1728\pi D^2 H}{4 \times 231}$$

In the alignment chart for this equation, shown in Fig. 9,

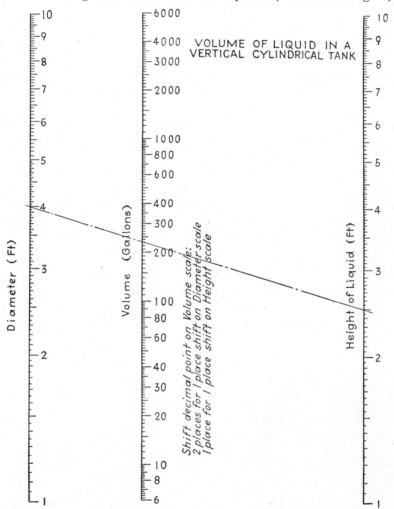

Fig. 9.—A simple Type 5 equation with logarithmic scales.

provision is made for shifts of the decimal point in the variables, and therefore only single cycles of the logarithmic scales for

D and H are used. These scales need not be identical in size as they are here, but equal-sized scales are most convenient. The D and H scales ascend in the same direction because they are multiplied together rather than divided one by the other.

The distance between the V scale line and other two scale lines is determined thus by formula:

$$g = \frac{\frac{1}{2}}{\frac{1}{2} + \frac{1}{1}} = \frac{d}{3}$$

If the construction method is preferred, any value of V, say 100 gal., is selected and two sets of values of D and H are determined which will yield 100 in the equation.

If $D = 2$,

$$H = \frac{4 \times 231 \times 100}{1728 \times 4 \times \pi} = 4.25$$

If $D = 3$,

$$H = \frac{4 \times 231 \times 100}{1728 \times 9 \times \pi} = 1.89$$

The size of the V scale logarithmic cycle is

$$\frac{n_V}{1} = \frac{g n_y}{db} = \frac{(d/3) n_y}{d \times 1} = \frac{n_y}{x}$$

It is also possible to determine that the V scale is one-third the size of the other two scales by solving the equation for V when D and H equal 1 and when they equal 10. In the latter instance V is 1000 times its value as determined for the former instance, indicating three cycles in the same space as one cycle of D or H. Before drawing in the V scale, it may be desirable to locate several points on its scale, such as 10, 100, and 1000, graphically, as a check.

In charting this equation no reference has been made to the constants $1728\pi/(4 \times 231)$. The reason for this is that they can be grouped with V and their only effect upon the completed alignment chart is in locating the V scale on the V scale line. Constants of this type do not affect position of scale lines or size of any scales.

TYPE 8

Nomogram for $f_1(x)\, f_2(y) = f_3(z)$ and $f_1(x)/f_2(y) = f_3(z)$

All equations considered so far may still be treated as special examples of the equation $f_1(x) + f_2(y) = f_3(z)$. The shorter method of using logarithmic function scales is described here.

The procedure for making a nomogram of function scales is identical in every respect with the procedure for the simple

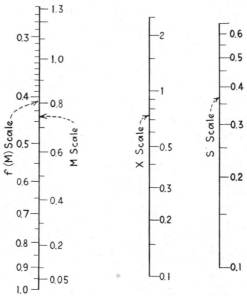

Fig. 10.—Simplified form of laying out bevel-gear nomogram. Logarithmic scales are used for functions of S and M.

formula $xy = z$, and the only additional step necessary to complete the nomogram is the replacement of the logarithmic scales of the functions with special scales of the variables.

The bevel-gear formula used in Fig. 5 with uniformly divided function scales may be placed in chart form more simply by using logarithmic function scales. The equation can be written:

$$\frac{S}{\left(1 - M + \dfrac{M^2}{3}\right)} = X$$

The limits of S are 0.1 to 0.65 and for M are 0.05 to 1.3. X varies from 0.1 to 2.50, and $f(M)$ from 0.263 to 0.950

$$f(M) = \left(1 - M + \frac{M^2}{3}\right).$$

If logarithmic scales of the functions of S and M are laid out as indicated in the procedure for the equation $x/y = z$, the result will be as indicated by the function scales in Fig. 10. The function scales for S and for X are in this instance the same as for S and X, and therefore need not be replaced. A table of values of M and $f(M)$ will be as follows:

M	$f(M)$	M	$f(M)$
0.1	0.9033	0.7	0.4633
0.2	0.8133	0.8	0.4133
0.3	0.7300	0.9	0.3700
0.4	0.6533	1.0	0.3333
0.5	0.5833	1.1	0.3033
0.6	0.5200	1.2	0.2800
		1.3	0.2633

NOMOGRAM FOR PIPE BENDS

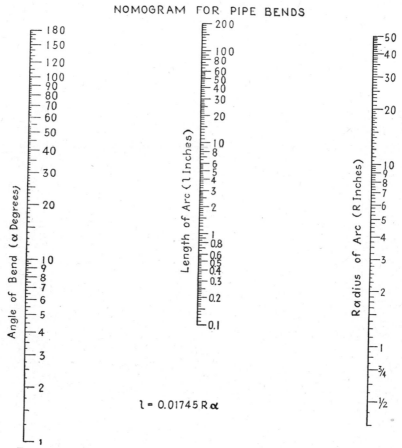

$$l = 0.01745 R \alpha$$

Fig. 11.—Where odd angles are involved it is much more convenient to lay a ruler across three scale lines than to worry over radian measure in the formula for the length of an arc.

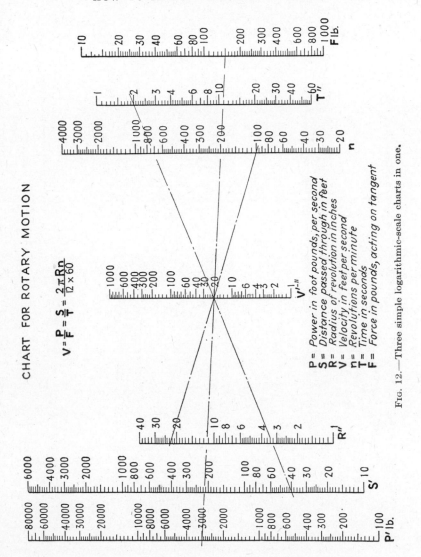

CHART FOR ROTARY MOTION

$$V = \frac{P}{F} = \frac{S}{T} = \frac{2\pi R n}{12 \times 60}$$

P = Power in foot pounds, per second
S = Distance passed through in feet
R = Radius of revolution in inches
V = Velocity in feet per second
n = Revolutions per minute
T = Time in seconds
F = Force in pounds, acting on tangent

FIG. 12.—Three simple logarithmic-scale charts in one.

CHART FOR DETERMINING CENTER OF GRAVITY, MOMENT OF
INERTIA AND SECTION MODULUS OF UNSYMMETRICAL SECTION

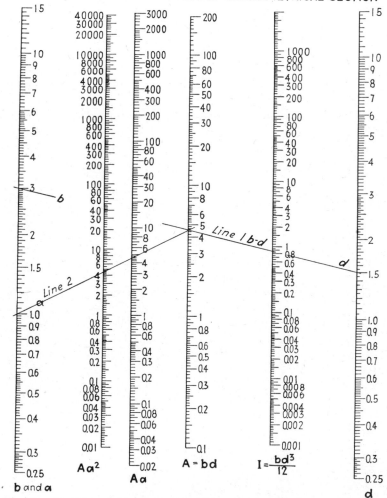

Fig. 13.—Each line of this combination chart gives two results useful in finding
the strength of unsymmetrical or built-up sections.

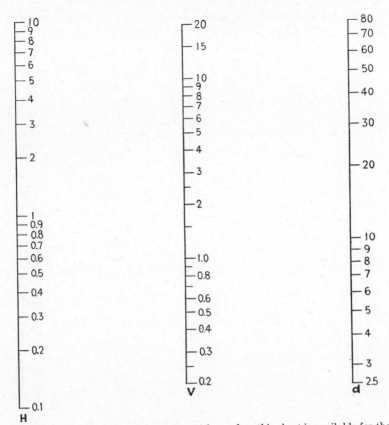

FIG. 14.—No need for multiplying logarithms when this chart is available for the equation $H = 8.4 \dfrac{V^{1.86}}{d^{1.25}}$.

TABLE I.—POSSIBLE ARRANGEMENTS OF EQUATION $R = 0.0194\ WSV^2$

1. $WS = X = R/0.0194V^2$ . . . .

2. $WV^2 = X = R/0.0194S$ . . . .

3. $WS = X$ and $0.0194V^2X = R$ . . . .

4. $R/W = X$ and $X/V^2 = 0.0194S$ . . . .

5. $R/X = 0.0194W$ and $SV^2 = X$ . . . .

6. $R/X = S$ and $0.0194W/X = 1/V^2$ . . . .

7. $X/S = W$ and $0.0194XV^2 = R$ . . . .

TYPE 9

Nomogram for $f_1(x) + f_2(y) + f_3(z) + \cdots = f_4(w)$ and for $f_1(x) \cdot f_2(y) \cdot f_3(z) \cdots = f_4(w)$

Any equation of four or more variables may be split up into two or more equations of three variables which may be charted by methods previously described. Thus the equation

$$R = 0.0194WSV^2$$

may be divided into two equations by introducing another variable X, which becomes a factor common to both equations. Some transpositions of this equation are given in the accompanying table with diagrams, convenient as a mental picture in visualizing the most desirable setup. Arrows indicate the direction of ascension of the function scales. [The direction of the

V scale in Eq. (6) in the table is opposite to the *f*(*V*) scale because *f*(*V*) = 1/*V*².] The constants may be attached to any variable.

The diagrams in the table are of use only as relating the scale positions but not the actual distances between the scale lines.

The two equations so formed by introduction of the variable *X* contain only three variables and may be treated by the rules previously laid out for the corresponding form, except when the *X* scale line is between the other two variables in the second equation. In this instance it is necessary to begin with the predeter-

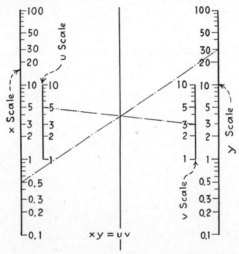

Fig. 15.—Nomogram for four variables as for equation $xy = uv$.

mined sizes of one outside scale and the intermediate scale instead of the two outside scales. This is because the size of the *X* scale has been fixed by the first of the two equations.

It requires careful planning for a nomogram of this kind to get the greatest advantage of a given size of sheet. For example, in Fig. 15, if the ranges of the four variables are such that two variables require three cycles of logarithmic scale and the other two variables require only one cycle of logarithmic scale, a grouping of the first two variables with *X* will produce a small-scale cycle of *X*. The single-cycle scales are therefore only one-third as long as the space allows. But if a three-cycle and a one-cycle scale are combined in an equation with *X*, the remaining equation will be similar, and all four scales will be the full length of the paper, as in Fig. 16. If the single-cycle scales of Fig. 15 had been drawn first to as large a scale as the space allows, the three-cycle scales would have overrun the available space on the sheet of paper.

The easiest construction results when the X scale line is between the other two in the first equation and is one of the outside scales in the second equation. The resulting nomogram may not be so economical of space but is satisfactory in most instances.

To obtain the largest possible scales in the second equation, those variables must be coupled in the first equation which will

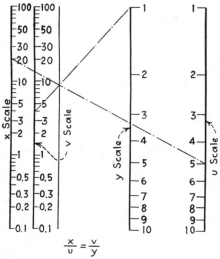

Fig. 16.—When the equation shown in Fig. 9 is in the form of $x/u = v/y$, all scale sizes can be drawn as large as the space allows.

give the largest scale for X. Other more important considerations, however, may influence the grouping.

Nomogram for Brake-band Pressure

An example, as in Fig. 17, will better illustrate the type in which the X or reference line is between the other two variables in both equations. The equation for maximum band pressure of brakes is

$$P = \frac{T}{Rb}$$

P = maximum band pressure = 40 to 400 lb. per square inch
T = tension or compression = 250 to 15,000 lb.
R = radius of the drum = 4 to 20 in.
b = width of the band = 1.5 to 6 in.

In this instance it is considered more important that R and b be coupled in one of the equations than that the greatest advantage be taken of the space, since both are dimensions.   The remaining

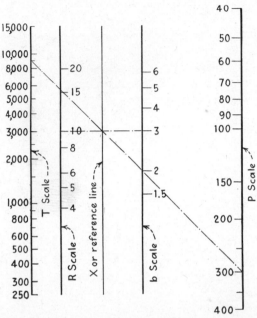

Fig. 17.—Chart layout of equation for maximum band pressure of a brake. Related variables such as dimensions or pressures are coupled.

two variables are also more nearly related.   The data is conveniently tabulated when the equation is written $T/P = Rb = X$.

	Limits	Cycles	Maximum cycle length, in.*	Actual cycle length, in.
P	40 to 400	1.0	10	10
T	250 to 15,000	1.8	5.5	5†
R	4 to 20	0.7	14	6.67
b	1.5 to 6	0.6	16.6	6.67
$X = (T/P)$	0.6 to 375	2.8		3.33
$X = (Rb)$	6 to 120			3.33

* Product of maximum cycle length × cycles = 10 in.
† Could be 5.5 in.   Standard log paper has a 5-in. cycle.

For $X = (T/P)$, distance $g_1 = d_1/3$.
For $X = (Rb)$, distance $g_2 = d_2/3$.

The *R* and *b* scales had to be shortened to keep the *P* and *T* scales within the limits of the paper. The number of possible

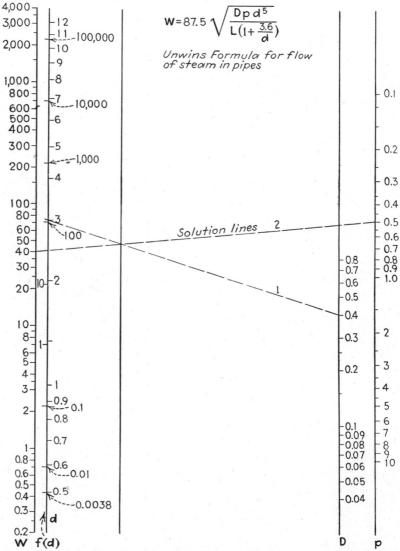

FIG. 18.—A mean formula with which to compute flow of steam is tamed with this chart.

scale lengths for *R* and *b* is unlimited: 6.67 and 6.67, 10 and 5, 15 and 4.285, etc. The first group, 6.67 and 6.67, was chosen because there is approximately the same percentage of a cycle in each scale. Simplicity of construction was also considered. Determination of these figures was from the equation

$$n_z = \frac{n_x n_y}{n_x + n_y} = \frac{10 \times 5}{10 + 5} = \frac{10}{3} \text{ (as applied to } \frac{T}{P} = X)$$

rearranged as a solution for n_x,

$$n_x = \frac{n_z n_y}{n_y - n_z} = \frac{10\!\!\!/_3 \times 20\!\!\!/_3}{20\!\!\!/_3 - 10\!\!\!/_3} = \frac{200\!\!\!/_9}{10\!\!\!/_3} = \frac{20}{3} \text{ (as applied to } Rb = X)$$

and from the simple rule that, when the outside function scales are equal in size, they are double the length of the middle function. Figure 17 shows the framework of the completed nomogram.

Five variables in the equation simply add another reference line. Each additional variable adds another reference line and another equation of three variables.

TYPE 10

Under some circumstances it is desirable to use uniformly divided scales for the division of two functions instead of logarithmic scales. Multiplication of functions can also be accomplished using two uniform scales by rearrangement of the equation. Advantages and disadvantages will become evident in the following procedure for the construction of Z charts.

THE Z CHART

The Z chart provides a means for nomographic solution of multiplication and division of functions in a formula without the necessity for logarithmic scales. Although the type form is shown as a division of functions, it is obvious that the product, xy, may be written $x/(1/y)$, and a reciprocal scale of y is used. But in many instances the use of the reciprocal scale is not desirable. One of the reasons for presenting alternate methods is to avoid undesirable scales.

Nomogram for $f_1(x)/f_2(y) = f_3(z)$

To lay out a Z chart as shown in Fig. 19, draw two parallel lines. Subdivide one line uniformly with a scale for $f_1(x)$ within the limits given and the other line similarly for $f_2(y)$ so that the two scales ascend in opposite directions.   The size of each scale is independent of the other and may be as large as the space allows for the given limits.   This is shown in Fig. 19.

The function scales are then replaced with scales of the variables in the equation as described under Type 4, page 7.

To locate the z scale or reference line, draw a diagonal line connecting the function values of zero on each of the parallel scales.

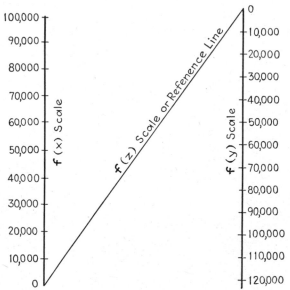

Fig. 19.—The Z chart for $f_1(x)/f_2(y) = f_3(z)$.   Uniformly divided scales ascend in opposite directions.   Scale sizes are independent of each other.

If the zero value is not included in the limits of the $f(x)$ and $f(y)$ scales, these scale lines are extended to include the zero value, or the location is computed from similar triangle ratios, as in Fig. 20, where $A/B = m/d$.   The line extensions are shown in dotted lines.

The z scale on the diagonal line may be produced by construction.   Select an upper value of $f(x)$ or corresponding value of x and solve the equation for $f(y)$ or y for a series of desired values of z.   Locate these values of z graphically on the diagonal line by drawing lines through the selected upper value of $f(x)$ or x and determine values of $f(y)$ or y corresponding to selected values of z.   Repeat with an upper value of $f(y)$ or corresponding value of y, solving for $f(x)$ or x until as many points as desired are located on the z scale line (see Appendix 4).

To be more specific, the equation for tension on bolts with U.S. standard threads is charted in Fig. 21:

$$D = 1.24\sqrt{\frac{L}{f}} + 0.088$$

D = outside diameter of the bolt in inches.

L = load on the bolt in pounds.

f = tension fiber stress in pounds per square inch.

The equation can be rewritten so that all the constants apply directly to the D scale:

$$\frac{L}{f} = \left(\frac{D - 0.088}{1.24}\right)^2$$

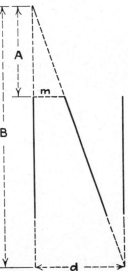

FIG. 20.—When zero values are not given, location of diagonal line is computed from similar-triangle ratios.

The selected upper value of L in Fig. 21 is 100,000.   The equation is solved for f, using this value of L and the values 1.5, 2, 3, and 4 for D_x.   The dotted lines in Fig. 21 locate the corresponding division lines on the D scale.   The selected upper value of f is also 100,000.   A similar process locates the values 1.25, 1, 0.75, 0.5, and 0.25 on the D scale line.   As many more points as desired can be located by this method.

When the equation $r/s = (100 - a)/a$ occurs, the diagonal scale line of the Z chart is uniformly divided as well as both vertical scales.   The nomogram for this equation is shown in Fig. 22.   The equation determines the resistance r of the slide wire of a Wheatstone bridge with a standard resistance s and a 100-unit length of wire with a slider at a distance a from one end.

To illustrate the advantage of a Z chart, a nomogram is shown in Fig. 23 for the equation

$$P_n = P(1 + r)^n$$

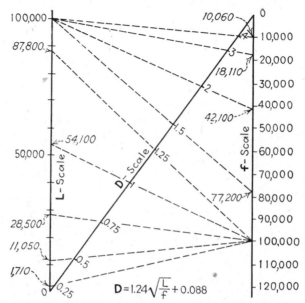

FIG. 21.—Method of locating values on the diagonal scale from upper values on both vertical scales.

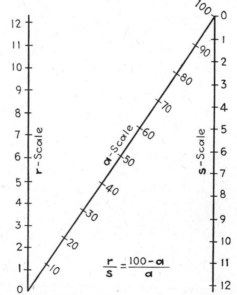

FIG. 22.—In an equation of the type $r/s = (100 - a)/a$, the diagonal scale is uniformly divided, as are both vertical scales.

which gives the total P_n for principal P plus compound interest at the end of n years at the interest rate r expressed in hundredths. The equation can be written

$$\log P_n - \log P = n \log (1 + r)$$

which may be arranged into two equations by introducing the variable function $\log X$ as follows:

$$\frac{\log (1 + r)}{\log X} = \frac{1}{n} \qquad \log X + \log P = \log P_n$$

The limits are as shown in Fig. 23. The limit for X was chosen as approximately the ratio of P_n/P resulting from 10 per cent

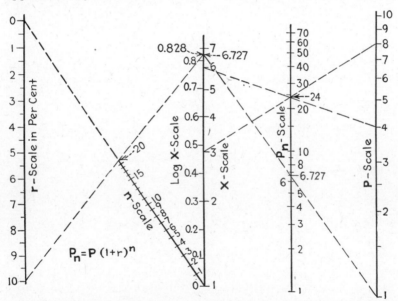

Fig. 23.—Nomogram for obtaining principal P plus compound interest at the end of n years at r rate of interest.

interest for 20 years. The quantity $(1 + r)$ varies from 1.01 to 1.10. The scale of r is logarithmic between the limits of 1.01 to 1.10, although the per cent scale is used, and the scale of X, if drawn, is also logarithmic.

The scales for r and X are drawn on parallel lines so that they ascend in opposite directions, each to as large a scale as the space allows. The diagonal scale line passes through the value of unity on the logarithmic scale of X, which corresponds to zero on the uniformly divided scale of the function log X, and through zero of the r scale, which corresponds with zero on the uniformly divided log $(1 + r)$ scale. The n scale is produced by passing lines through computed values of log X and the point 10 on the r scale. The intersections on the diagonal line determine corresponding values of n, the number of years.

The scale of n may be completely laid out by using an equation derived from that relating r, X, and n, in which the selected upper value of $f(r)$ is 1.10:

$$\log X = n \log 1.10$$

A table of values of log X for chosen values of n will assist in locating scale divisions.

n	log X	n	log X
1	0	11	1.041
2	0.301	12	1.079
3	0.477	13	1.114
4	0.602	14	1.146
5	0.699	15	1.176
6	0.778	16	1.204
7	0.845	17	1.230
8	0.903	18	1.255
9	0.954	19	1.279
10	1.000	20	1.301

The second half of the chart, namely, scales P and P_n, is constructed as previously described under the logarithmic type equation shown and explained under Type 5, page 11. Construction lines for locating the P_n scale line are shown and solution lines to indicate that P_n is $6727 when P = $1000, r = 10 per cent interest, and n = 20 years:

$$P_n = \$1000(1 + 0.10)^{20} = \$6727$$

It is obvious that the nomograms under Types 1 to 9, inclusive, are not adequate to handle the preceding example nor the following equation solving for the moment of inertia of a prism:

$$I = \frac{W}{12}(h^2 + b^2)$$

When the equation is divided into two parts,

$$12I/W = X = h^2 + b^2,$$

the X scale would be logarithmic for one equation and uniformly divided for the other by methods previously described. The Z chart, as shown in Fig. 24, makes the X scale a uniformly divided

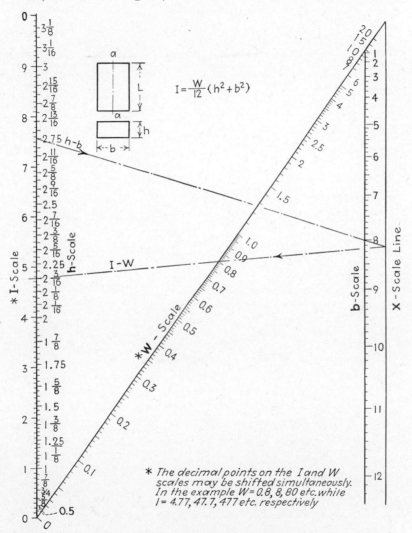

$$I = \frac{W}{12}(h^2 + b^2)$$

* *The decimal points on the I and W scales may be shifted simultaneously. In the example W = 0.8, 8, 80 etc. while I = 4.77, 47.7, 477 etc. respectively*

FIG. 24.—Z chart for determining the moment of inertia of a prism about the a-a axis as shown in the diagram.

scale identical for both equations. It is not necessary to sub-divide the X scale, although it is done in Fig. 23 for demonstration, since it becomes merely a reference line.

The hygrometry chart of Fig. 25 is unique in several respects. It consists of three Z charts in one, including a four-variable equation the other half of which is a Type 4 equation. The

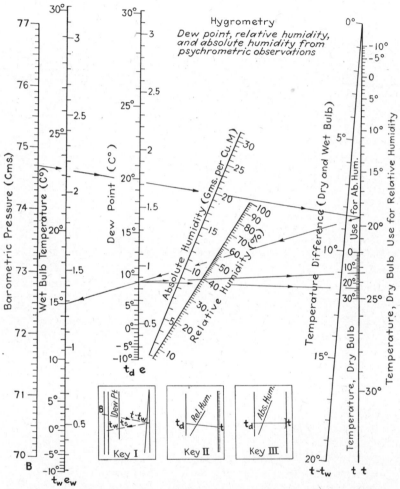

FIG. 25.—Hygrometry data as derived from Smithsonian data but without tedious computation and reference to tables.

three results are conveniently grouped on the center three scale lines.

Determinations of dew point, relative humidity, and absolute humidity may be made as indicated in Keys I, II, and III, respectively. Having given barometric pressure, B; difference between dry- and wet-bulb temperatures, $t - t_w$; and wet-bulb temperature, t_w; the dew point, t_d, may be determined as indicated in Key I. This process solves the equation

$$e = e_w - 0.00066B(t - t_w)[1 + 0.00115(t - t_w)]$$

in which e and e_w are vapor pressures. The former is the actual pressure at the dry-bulb temperature and at the same time the maximum pressure possible at the dew point. The latter is the maximum possible pressure at the wet-bulb temperature. The whole quantity to the right of B is a function of $(t - t_w)$.

Instead of having a formula to express the relation between e and the corresponding temperatures, the temperature scales were determined from a table of empirical data. The letters e and e_w may be considered as functions of dew point, $f(t_d)$, and of wet-bulb temperature, $f(t_w)$. Scales for e on the wet-bulb and dew-point temperature scales are unnecessary to the chart, being function scales.

Dew-point and dry-bulb temperatures are sufficient to determine humidity. Relative humidity is the ratio of actual vapor pressure to the maximum possible pressure at the same temperature. These are both the same function of temperature. Therefore $R = f(t_d)/f(t)$. Absolute humidity is determined from the formula

$$A = \frac{10.60e}{1 + 0.00367t}$$

The diagonal lines in none of the three charts extend from one parallel scale line to the other. The $(t - t_w)$ scale line, however, is in line with zero of the B scale, and humidity scale lines are in line with zeros of two different functions of dry-bulb temperature as well as zero of the e scale.

It is possible to reproduce scales not only from tabulated data for which there is no simple formula relation but also from empirical or experimentally determined curves or plotted points where formulas are too complicated to be expressed mathematically.

TYPE 11

THE DOUBLE Z CHART

Nomogram for $f_1(x)/f_2(y) = f_3(u)/f_4(v)$

In laying out a double Z chart, two parallel lines are drawn, one subdivided uniformly with a scale for $f_1(x)$ as in Fig. 26, within the limits given, and the other similarly for $f_2(y)$ so that the two

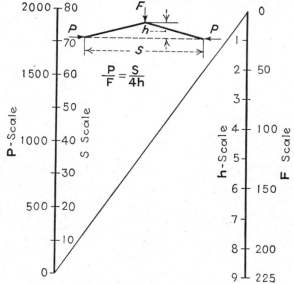

Fig. 26.—A typical example of a double Z chart.

scales ascend in opposite directions. The size of each scale is independent of the other but should be planned in consideration of the following relation:

$$\frac{m_x}{m_y} = \frac{m_u}{m_v}$$

in which m is the length of a function unit. In other words, the scales of $f_3(u)$ and $f_4(v)$ should be visualized before determining definitely the size of the $f_1(x)$ and $f_2(y)$ scales.

To locate the diagonal reference line, draw a diagonal line between the function values of zero on the $f_1(x)$ and $f_2(y)$ scales. If this value is not included in the limits, either extend the line or compute the location from similar-triangle ratios as in Fig. 20.

THE *u* AND *v* SCALES

The *u* and *v* scales may be located on any two parallel lines such that the zeros of the $f_3(u)$ and $f_4(v)$ scales coincide with the zero of the $f_1(x)$ and $f_2(y)$ scales, respectively. The size of the $f_3(u)$ and $f_4(v)$ scale units may be as large as the space allows, but

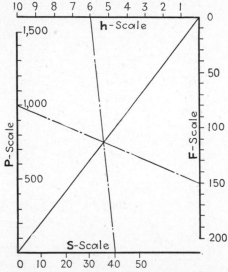

FIG. 27.—The same chart as in Fig. 26 but with two scale lines turned through 90 deg.

the relation between their sizes must be the same as that between the $f_1(x)$ and $f_2(y)$ scales, as expressed in the formula

$$\frac{m_x}{m_y} = \frac{m_u}{m_v}$$

All function scales are replaced with scales of the variables as described under Type 4 on page 7.

Both the nomograms shown in Figs. 26 and 27 are for the equation for finding the relations of forces and dimensions of a toggle joint. Scales for *P* and *F* in Fig. 26 are drawn first. Using a maximum length for the *h* scale, the *S* scale is limited to a shorter space by the given relation between unit lengths. It is usually a matter of trial to obtain the most satisfactory arrangement. This formula works out more satisfactorily with the logarithmic-scale type of nomogram.

Every different type of nomogram permits new combinations and arrangements, which often are valuable merely as a means of making the solution of equations more obvious. The type shown in Fig. 27 is adaptable only to equations of four or more variables. The solution lines, instead of intersecting at a com-

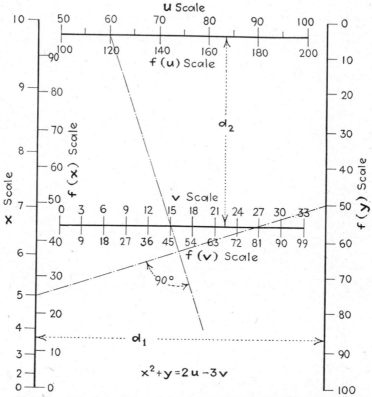

Fig. 28.—Location of parallel u and v scale lines is independent of parallel x and y scale lines.

mon point on a reference line are either parallel or perpendicular to each other, and the reference line is eliminated.

There are a number of arrangements in which nomograms can be shown. When equations contain four or more variables, the scale lines can be drawn in both vertical or horizontal positions. The solution lines do not intersect at a common point but are either parallel or perpendicular to each other. One advantage of this is that it avoids the confusion resulting from four or more

parallel scale lines.   Such a chart is dependent upon a guide to
solution or a key sketch.   The question of which two scale lines
should be crossed by a given solution line is obvious in nomograms
laid out according to the following plan:

TYPE 12

NOMOGRAMS WITH PARALLEL OR PERPENDICULAR SOLUTION LINES

Nomogram for $f_1(x) \pm f_2(y) = f_3(u) \pm f_4(v)$

In laying out a nomogram having perpendicular solution lines
as shown in Fig. 28, two parallel lines are subdivided uniformly

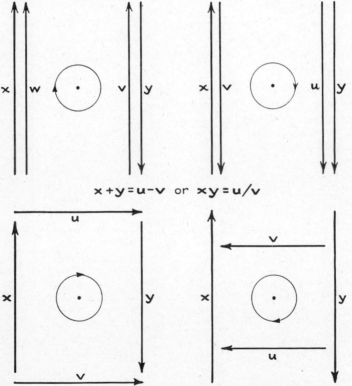

Fig. 29.—Scales ascend in same rotational direction when functions are sub-
tracted or divided, and in opposite directions when functions are added or
multiplied.

with scales of $f_1(x)$ and $f_2(y)$ ascending in opposite directions if
the sign between them is plus and in the same direction if the

sign is minus. The sizes of the function scale units must be the same.

The u and v scale lines are drawn parallel to the x and y scale lines or perpendicular to them. Their location is independent

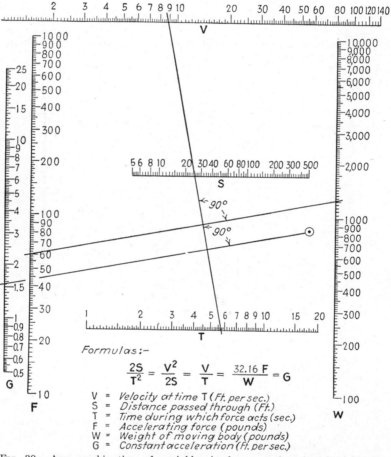

CHART FOR ACCELERATED MOTION

Formulas:—

$$\frac{2S}{T^2} = \frac{V^2}{2S} = \frac{V}{T} = \frac{32.16\ F}{W} = G$$

V = Velocity at time T (Ft. per sec.)
S = Distance passed through (Ft.)
T = Time during which force acts (sec.)
F = Accelerating force (pounds)
W = Weight of moving body (pounds)
G = Constant acceleration (Ft. per sec.)

Fig. 30.—Any combination of variables in four equations is solved in this Type 12 chart.

of the first pair of lines. The size of the $f_3(u)$ and $f_4(v)$ scales must be the same, and their relation to the size of the $f_1(x)$ and $f_2(y)$ scales is determined by the rule

$$\frac{m_x}{m_u} = \frac{d_1}{d_2}$$

m = length of function scale units designated by subscript.

d_1 = distance between the x and y scale lines.

d_2 = distance between the u and v scale lines.

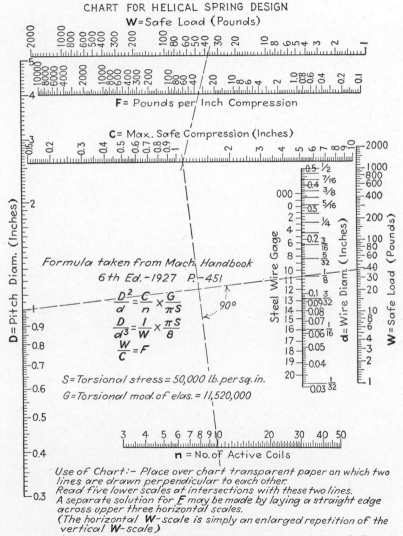

FIG. 31.—Much confusion is saved here by turning some of the scale lines at right angles to the others. The trick was in making the same D and d scales serve in two equations when both functions differed in the two equations.

Either line is subdivided with a uniform scale of $f_3(u)$ within its limits and ascending in the same rotational direction as the

$f_1(x)$ scale, as illustrated in Fig. 29 for the equation $x + y = u - v$. The $f_4(v)$ scale ascends in a direction opposite to the $f_3(u)$ scale if the sign between them is plus and in the same direction if the sign is minus.

The position of the $f_4(v)$ or v scale on the fourth line in Fig. 28 is relative to some starting point determined by selecting a value within its range and determining values of the other three functions which will satisfy the equation. A line drawn across the $f_1(x)$ and $f_2(y)$ scales at the determined values will give the slope of a line which, drawn through the third known point, will locate the selected value on the fourth scale. Thus, assuming $v = 15$ is selected as the starting point, any values of x and y are selected, such as 5 and 50, respectively. Then in the equation which is charted in Fig. 28,

$$u = \frac{(x^2 + y + 3v)}{2} = \frac{(25 + 50 + 45)}{2} = 60$$

The solution lines then locate 15 on the v scale.

After determining the $f_4(v)$ scale, all function scales are replaced with scales of the corresponding variables as described under Type 4 on page 7 (see Appendix 5).

TYPE 13

Nomogram for $f_1(x) \cdot f_2(y) = f_3(u) \cdot f_4(v)$ or for $f_1(x)/f_2(y) = f_3(u)/f_4(v)$

The nomogram in Fig. 32 is another form of the same equation used in Fig. 26, page 38. Two parallel lines are subdivided with logarithmic scales of $f_1(x)$ and $f_2(y)$. They ascend in opposite directions if the functions are multiplied, and in the same direction if one function is divided by the other. The sizes of the function-scale cycles must be the same.

For the u and v scales, two lines are drawn parallel to each other, and either parallel to the x and y scale lines or perpendicular to them. Their location is independent of the first pair of lines. The sizes of the $f_3(u)$ and $f_4(v)$ cycles must be the same and their relation to the sizes of the $f_1(x)$ and $f_2(y)$ logarithmic cycles is determined by the following rule:

$$\frac{n_x}{n_u} = \frac{d_1}{d_2}$$

n = length of the function-scale logarithmic cycles designated
     by subscript.

d_1 = distance between x and y scale lines.

d_2 = distance between u and v scale lines.

Either line is subdivided with a logarithmic scale of $f_3(u)$ within its limits and ascending in the same rotational direction as the $f_1(x)$ scale, as in Fig. 31. The $f_4(v)$ scale ascends in a direction opposite to the $f_3(u)$ scale if the functions are multiplied and in the same direction if the functions are divided. The position of the function scale on the line is relative to some starting point determined by selecting a value of $f_4(v)$ or v within its range and determining values of the other three functions which will satisfy the equation.

A line drawn across the $f_1(x)$ and $f_2(y)$ scales at the determined values will give the slope of a line which, drawn through the third known point, locates the selected value on the fourth scale line. After determining the $f_4(v)$ scale, all function scales are replaced with scales of the corresponding variables as described under Type 4 on page 7.

To illustrate the nomogram for $f_1(x)/f_2(y) = f_3(u)/f_4(v)$ in Fig. 32, the toggle joints with equal arms act in the relation

$$\frac{P}{F} = \frac{S}{4h}$$

where P is the pressure resulting from a force F, and S and h are dimensions as indicated in the diagram. $P = 10$ to $10{,}000$ lb.; $F = 1$ to 250 lb.; $S = 4$ to 40 in.; and $h = 0.1$ to 10 in. If $f(S) = S/4$, $f(S) = 1$ to 10.

Scales of $f(S)$ and h are made as large as the space allows with equal length cycles and ascending in the same direction. The P scale, having three cycles to two of the h scale, must be drawn to a smaller scale, not larger than $\frac{2}{3}$ the size of the h cycle. Therefore the distance between the P and F scale lines must be not more than $\frac{2}{3}$ the distance between the S and h scale lines. In other words, assuming $n_h = 1$ and $n_p = \frac{2}{3}$, if $d_1 = 1$, then $d_2 = \frac{2}{3}$ from the given proportion.

The P scale is then drawn with this shortened cycle, and the point $F = 1$ is selected on the F scale. When $h = 0.1$ and $f(S) = 1$, $P = 10$. A line through the lower scale ends drawn through $P = 10$ locates 1 on the F scale. The scale of F can then be drawn with the same cycle as the P scale, ascending in the same direction. With increased familiarity with the method it may not be necessary to produce both the function scale and the scale of the variable.

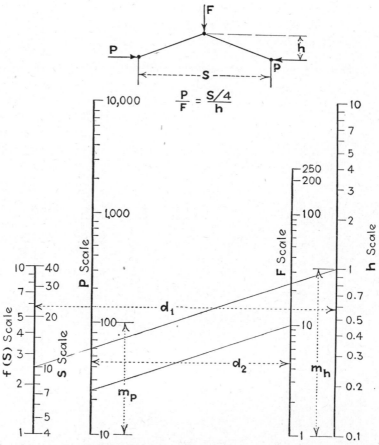

Fig. 32.—Nomogram illustrating the application of equation $f_1(x)/f_2(y) = f_3(u)/f_4(v)$ for toggle joints with equal arms.

TYPE 14

Nomogram for $f_1(x) + f_2(y) = f_3(u)/f_4(v)$

Parallel solution lines can also be applied to the Z chart for an equation in the form $x + y = u/v$. To lay out such a nomogram, as shown in Fig. 33, two parallel lines are subdivided uniformly with scales of $f_1(x)$ and $f_2(y)$ so that they ascend in opposite directions. The size of the function units must be the same. The diagonal line is drawn between the zeros of the two scales.

The u scale is obtained by first subdividing the opposite side of the $f_1(x)$ scale with a uniformly divided scale of $f_3(u)$ so that the

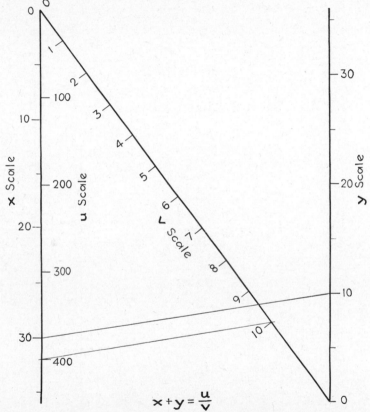

$$x + y = \frac{u}{v}$$

Fig. 33.—Z chart construction of $x + y = u/v$ showing graphically how uniformly divided diagonal scale is located.

zeros of both scales coincide. The scale may be as large as the space allows.

A uniformly divided scale of $f_4(v)$ may be located graphically on the diagonal line by subdividing, with equal divisions, the line between zero, which coincides with zero of the $f_3(u)$ scale, and its upper limit. The upper limit of the $f_4(v)$ scale can be located by drawing a line through values of $f_1(x)$ and $f_2(y)$, the sum of which equals $f_3(u)_{max}$ divided by $f_4(v)_{max}$. A parallel line through $f_3(u)_{max}$ on the scale will locate $f_4(v)_{max}$ on the diagonal line. Thus

$$\frac{f_3(u)_{max}}{f_4(v)_{max}} = \frac{400}{10} = 40 = 30 + 10 \text{ (or other values whose sum is 40)}$$

A line drawn through $u = 400$, parallel to the line through $x = 30$ and $y = 10$, locates $v = 10$ on the diagonal line.

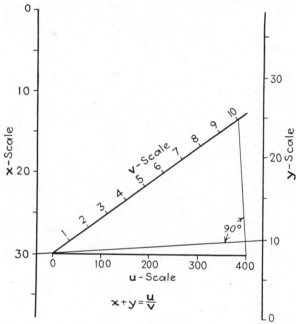

Fig. 34.—The same nomogram as in Fig. 33 but with u and v scales turned through 90 deg.

The size of the $f_4(v)$ scale unit m_v may be computed from the $f_3(u)$ scale unit and the number of units, k, of the $f_1(x)$ scale which may be placed on the diagonal line. Thus

$$m_v = km_u$$

For this relation, $k = 44.41$ in Fig. 33, k being the measured length of the diagonal in x units.

In other forms of this nomogram the u and v scales may be placed on any two lines that are parallel or perpendicular to the x scale line and the diagonal line. The zeros of the $f_3(u)$ and

$f_4(v)$ scales must coincide as before with the intersection of the two lines, and, in the latter case, the solution lines will be perpendicular to each other also. Fig. 34 shows a nomogram for the same equation as Fig. 33 but with the u and v scales turned through 90 deg. (see Appendix 6).

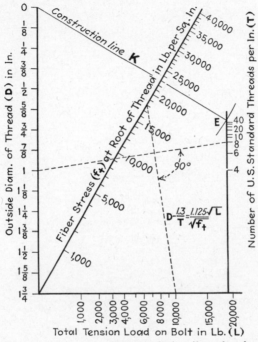

FIG. 35.—Nomogram with perpendicular solution lines for determining bolt diameters.

If the sign between $f_1(x)$ and $f_2(y)$ is negative, the $f_2(y)$ scale extends below the zero value shown in Fig. 33 instead of above this point. An example of this type is shown in Fig. 35, a chart for determining bolt diameters. The construction line K is the diagonal line to which reference has been made above. In this instance, the scales corresponding to u and v are on lines that are perpendicular to the scale corresponding to x and to the diagonal line. In this respect it is similar to Fig. 34. The functions of the equation

$$D - \frac{1.3}{T} = \frac{1.125\sqrt{L}}{\sqrt{f_t}}$$

are $f(D) = D$; $f(T) = 1.3/T$; $f(L) = 1.125\sqrt{L}$; and $f(f_t) = \sqrt{f_t}$. In the example, a 1-in. diameter bolt having eight threads per inch and under a tension of 10,000 lb. has a fiber stress of 18,000 lb. at the root of the thread.

TYPE 15

Nomogram for $\dfrac{x + y}{x - y} = \dfrac{f_1(u)}{f_2(v)}$ **or** $\dfrac{f_1(x) + f_2(y)}{f_1(x) - f_2(y)} = \dfrac{f_3(u)}{f_4(v)}$

In laying out a nomogram for such an equation, four lines are drawn as shown in Fig. 36, intersecting at a point such that the

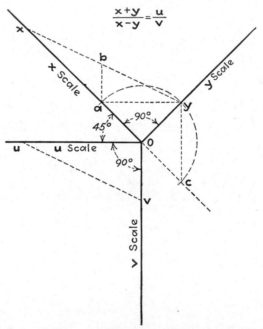

Fig. 36.—The four scale lines, radiating from a common intersection point, form angles of 90, 45 and 90 deg., respectively.

angles between successive lines are respectively 90 deg., 45 deg., and 90 deg. The two lines separated by an angle of 45 deg. are subdivided with uniformly divided scales of $f_1(x)$ and $f_3(u)$ of any convenient sizes independently of each other so that zero of each scale is at the intersection of the lines. A uniformly divided scale of $f_2(y)$ of the same size as the $f_1(x)$ scale is placed on the line at right angles with the $f_1(x)$ scale line so that zero is at the intersection. A uniformly divided scale of $f_4(v)$ of the same size as the $f_3(u)$ scale is placed on the line at right angles with the $f_3(u)$ scale line so that zero is at the intersection. The function scales are then replaced with scales of the variables. In this example the solution lines are parallel, but, by swinging one pair of the perpendicular lines 90 deg. toward the other pair less

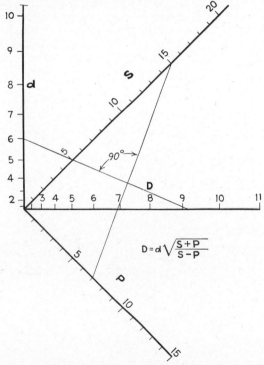

$$D = d\sqrt{\frac{S+P}{S-P}}$$

Fig. 37.—Nomogram of Lame's formula for determining the stresses in thick-walled cylinders.

space is required and similar results are obtained with perpendicular solution lines (see Appendix 7).

This type of nomogram is of a more special character than other types that have been treated heretofore. The example given in Fig. 37 is Lame's formula for stresses in thick-walled cylinders:

$$D = d\sqrt{\frac{S+P}{S-P}}$$

The external and internal diameters, d and D, are in the same units, and the stress and pressure, S and P, are in similar units.

TYPE 16

In nomograms involving either parallel or perpendicular solution lines, it is obvious that the relation of similar triangles applies and that differences in the sizes of the scales can be expressed mathematically by the proper evaluation of constants introduced into the equations.   A nomogram that is similar

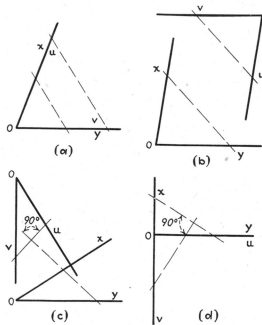

Fig. 38.—Parallel solution lines are used at a and b, while at c and d perpendicular solution lines are used.

to that shown in Fig. 40 can be made of the following equation, except for the angular relationships.

Nomogram for $f_1(x)/f_2(y) = f_3(u)/f_4(v)$

In Fig. 38(a), the two lines, intersecting at any angle, are subdivided with uniformly divided scales of $f_1(x)$ and $f_2(y)$ so that zero of each scale is at the intersection, as at O in the illustration. The size of each scale is independent of the other and may be as

large as the space allows. Four alternatives are common in
placing the $f_3(u)$ and $f_4(v)$ scales, which are uniformly subdivided
on lines making the same angle with each other as the lines on
which the $f_1(x)$ and $f_2(y)$ scales are drawn. At a, the opposite
sides of the same two lines are used. At b, lines parallel with
$f_1(x)$ and $f_2(y)$ scale lines and swung around 180 deg. are used.
At c and d, lines perpendicular to the $f_1(x)$ and $f_2(y)$ scale lines are
shown in two of many possible positions. Zeros of the $f_3(u)$ and

Fig. 39.—Nomogram for relation of volume and temperature of gases when the
pressure is constant.

$f_4(v)$ scales are also at the intersections O of the second pair
of lines. These scales need not be the same size as the $f_1(x)$ and
$f_2(y)$ scales, but must have the same relative size to each other
so that

$$\frac{m_x}{m_y} = \frac{m_u}{m_v}$$

where m is the size of the scale units.

The foregoing procedure is illustrated in Fig. 39, relating volume and temperature of gases, the pressure being constant:

$$\frac{v_1}{v_2} = \frac{273 + t_1}{273 + t_2}$$

where t = centigrade temperature.

If a larger angle were drawn between scales, in this instance a much smaller scale of t would be necessary. The nomogram is shown complete with the centigrade temperature scales, t_1 and t_2, replacing the function scales of absolute temperature, the limits of which are 373 to 483; $f(t) = 273 + t$, or $273 + 100$, to $273 + 210$, as illustrated.

Combination nomograms consisting of the above type and other forms with parallel or perpendicular solution lines are also possible. The nomogram for determining bolt diameters in Fig. 35 on page 49 is a good example.

TYPE 17

Except for short ranges the reciprocal scale, generally speaking, is to be avoided. The following method avoids three reciprocal scales at once.

Nomogram for $\dfrac{1}{f_1(x)} + \dfrac{1}{f_2(y)} = \dfrac{1}{f_3(z)}$

It is well to recognize that another form of this equation is

$$f_3(z) = \frac{f_1(x)f_2(y)}{f_1(x) + f_2(y)}$$

In laying out a nomogram for an equation of this type, two intersecting lines are drawn as shown in Fig. 40. Each line is subdivided with uniform scales of $f_1(x)$ and $f_2(y)$ independently of each other and of any convenient size such that zero of each scale will be at the intersection.

To locate the z scale line, select a value of $f_3(z)$ larger than its maximum value, such as 10 in the nomogram, and draw lines from the same values of $f_1(x)$ and $f_2(y)$, the former parallel to the $f_2(y)$ scale line and the latter parallel to the $f_1(x)$ scale line. The intersection of the two lines locates the selected value of $f_3(z)$ on the $f_3(z)$ scale. The $f_3(z)$ scale line is a diagonal of the parallelogram so formed.

To obtain the size of the $f_3(z)$ scale unit, the $f_3(z)$ scale is subdivided with equal divisions between the selected value and zero at the intersection of the three scale lines. The selected value is obviously outside the practical limit of the $f_3(z)$ scale in Fig. 40 because a line through maximum values of $f_1(x)$ and $f_2(y)$ intersects the $f_3(z)$ scale just beyond 6.

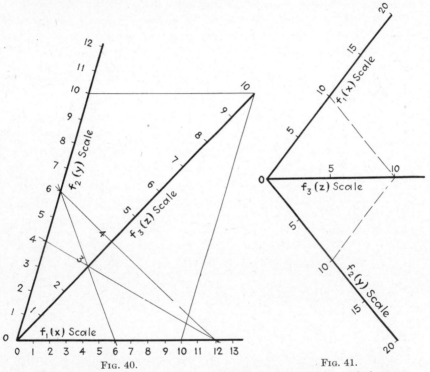

Fɪɢ. 40.   Fɪɢ. 41.

Fɪɢs. 40, 41.—In a nomogram having either an acute or obtuse angle between the two indicating scales, the *z* scale is the diagonal of the parallelogram.

This type of nomogram is suitable for determining the value of electrical resistances in a parallel circuit, focal length of lenses, and similar formulas. Figure 41 is another form of Fig. 40 with an obtuse angle between the $f_1(x)$ and $f_2(y)$ (see Appendix 8).

NOMOGRAMS WITH CURVED SCALES

Thus far, nomograms having only straight-line scales have been shown, and the corresponding equations or formulas have contained but one function of any variable. Curved scale lines are used in the following nomograms for equations having more than one function of any variable.

TYPE 18

Nomogram for $f_1(u) \, f_3(v) + f_2(u) \, f_4(w) = 1$

Equations or formulas of this type are not usually written in the above form, but are commonly written

$$f_3(v) = f_1(u) \pm f_4(w)f_2(u)$$

which is reducible to the type form by dividing through by $f_1(u)$ and rearranging the terms. Reduction to the type form is required to determine the proper function scales of $f_3(v)$ and $f_4(w)$. Thus, to illustrate this reduction in the equation,

$$C = \frac{0.2416L}{\log_{10} \dfrac{2L}{d}}$$

The functions C and d are not the usable functions, but $1/C$ and $\log d$ are the usable functions. Rewritten, the equation becomes

$$\left(\frac{1}{C}\right)\left(\frac{0.2416L}{\log 2L}\right) + \left(\frac{1}{\log 2L}\right)(\log d) = 1$$

The simplest construction of a nomogram of this type is by the graphical method. Two possibilities are available with parallel scale lines for v and w scales, namely, uniformly divided scales of $f_3(v)$ and $f_4(w)$ ascending in the same direction or in opposite directions. The writer has found it preferable in most instances to use the arrangement by which the u or curved scale will be placed between the v and w scales, this being determined by trial.

GRAPHICAL METHOD

In using the graphical method, as shown in Fig. 42, two parallel lines are drawn. One line is subdivided uniformly with a scale for $f_3(v)$ within the limits given and the other similarly for $f_4(w)$ so that the two scales ascend in opposite directions. One point is located on the u scale as directed in the following paragraphs, and, if this point lies outside the parallel scale lines, one scale is reversed so that the $f_3(v)$ and $f_4(w)$ scales ascend in the same direction. The size of each scale is independent of the other and may be as large as the space allows for the given limits.

To locate the u scale line, a value of $f_3(v)$ or $f_4(w)$ is selected and the original equation is solved for $f_4(w)$ or $f_3(v)$, respectively, for a set of values of u, which are to be placed on the u scale.

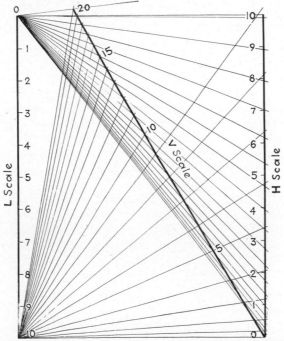

Fig. 42.—Graphical method of laying out a nomogram for obtaining the curved scale.

The process is repeated for another value of $f_3(v)$ or $f_4(w)$, using the same values of u. The intersections of lines corresponding to the same value of u will locate values of u on the u scale. Function scales may then be replaced with scales of the v and w variables.

To illustrate the foregoing two paragraphs, the formula

$$H = 0.0274V^2 + 0.0141LV^{1.83}$$

gives the friction losses in condenser tubes L feet long when the velocity of water is V feet per second. Written in the type form, the formula becomes

$$\frac{H}{0.0274V^2} - \frac{0.0141LV^{1.83}}{0.0274V^2} = 1$$

L and H can, therefore, be used as they appear in the formula.

In Fig. 42 uniformly divided scales of L and H are drawn on parallel lines with scales ascending in opposite directions. A check computation of H for the value of $V = 10$ when $L = 0$ and when $L = 10$ reveals that the V scale will lie between the L and H scale lines. A set of values of H can then be determined from the equation

$$H = 0.0274V^2 \qquad \text{when} \qquad L = 0$$

and another set from the equation

$$H = 0.0274V^2 + 0.0141(10V^{1.83}) \qquad \text{when} \qquad L = 10$$

A series of values is tabulated below, in which H_0 corresponds to $L = 0$ and H_{10} to $L = 10$. The manner of plotting the V scale is shown in Fig. 42.

V	H_0	H_{10}	V	H_0	H_{10}
1	0.0274	0.168	11	3.315	14.63
2	0.1096	0.528	12	3.945	17.20
3	0.2466	1.162	13	4.63	20.03
4	0.438	2.030	14	5.37	22.94
5	0.685	3.37	15	6.16	26.11
6	0.987	4.73	16	7.02	29.61
7	1.343	6.30	17	7.92	33.02
8	1.754	8.08	18	8.88	36.73
9	2.22	10.06	19	9.89	40.69
10	2.74	12.27	20	10.96	44.76

The following series of examples illustrates the type of equation that can be solved nomographically by this method and also gives the transformation of the equation to the type form.

1. Radius R of a circle having a chord of length c and sagitta h.

$$R = \frac{c^2 + 4h^2}{8h} \qquad R\left(\frac{2}{h}\right) + c^2\left(-\frac{1}{4h^2}\right) = 1 \quad \text{(see Figs. 50 and 51)}$$

2. Stadia formula for horizontal distance in which H is the horizontal distance in feet, R is the rod reading multiplied by 100,

a is the vertical angle, and c is the instrument constant.

$$H = R \cos^2 a + c \cos a \qquad H\left(\frac{1}{c \cos a}\right) + R\left(-\frac{\cos a}{c}\right) = 1$$

3. Quadratic equations.

$$x^2 + Px + Q = 0 \qquad \frac{P}{-x} + \frac{Q}{-x^2} = 1 \text{ (see Fig. 57)}$$

$$cx^2 + x + d = 0 \qquad c(-x) + d\left(\frac{-1}{x}\right) = 1 \text{ (see Fig. 58)}$$

4. Kepler's equation (important in astronomy) in which nt and θ are angles in radians and e is the eccentricity of the orbit of a planet.

$$nt = \theta - e \sin \theta \qquad nt\left(\frac{1}{\theta}\right) + e\left(\frac{\sin \theta}{\theta}\right) = 1$$

5. A trigonometric equation.

$$a \tan x + b \sec x + 1 = 0 \qquad a\,(-\tan x) + b(-\sec x) = 1$$

6. A power equation.

$$bx = a^x \qquad \log a\,\left(\frac{x}{\log x}\right) + \log b\,\left(\frac{-1}{\log x}\right) = 1 \text{ (see Fig. 47)}$$

7. Hydraulics. Average velocity, V, in feet per second through a rectangular orifice under low head. The depth from the surface of the liquid to the bottom of the orifice is h_1 and to the top, h_2. Acceleration of gravity, g, is the constant.

$$V = \frac{2\sqrt{2g}}{3}\left(\frac{\sqrt{h_1{}^3} - \sqrt{h_1{}^3}}{h_1 - h_2}\right) \text{ (see Fig. 59)}$$

$$V\left(\frac{h_2}{\frac{2}{3}\sqrt{2g}\,\sqrt[3]{h_2{}^2}}\right) + N\left(\frac{-1}{\frac{2}{3}\sqrt{2g}\,\sqrt[3]{h_2{}^2}}\right) = 1$$

The same equation can be written for h_1, supplying the same variable, N. The equations are identical and the values of h_1 and h_2 are on the same curved scale. The scale for N may be omitted in the final chart. A nomogram for this equation is given in Fig. 59.

8. Volume of a frustrum of a pyramid where h is the height, A_1 the area of the top, and A_2 the area of the bottom. A nomogram

of this equation is illustrated in Fig. 60.

$$V = \frac{h}{3}(A_1 + A_2 + \sqrt{A_1 A_2})$$

$$\frac{3V}{h} = \frac{\sqrt{A_1{}^3} - \sqrt{A_2{}^3}}{\sqrt{A_1} - \sqrt{A_2}} \qquad \left(\frac{3V}{h}\right)\left(\frac{1}{A}\right) + N\left(\frac{-1}{\sqrt{A^3}}\right) = 1$$

THE PLOTTING METHOD

For locating and subdividing the u scale, as in Fig. 43, let x and y represent the following values taken from the equation under Type 18.

$$x = \frac{-f_2(u)}{f_1(u) + f_2(u)} \qquad y = \frac{1}{f_1(u) + f_2(u)} \text{ (Appendix 9)}$$

A table is made of the values of x and y for each value of u which it is desired to show on the u scale line, and the values are plotted on graph paper in rectangular coordinates. The size of a unit of x is the distance between the parallel scale lines for the v and w scales and the size of a unit of y is identical with that of a unit of $f_3(v)$ and $f_4(w)$.

In locating the v and w scale lines as in Fig. 43, the $f_3(v)$ scale line is uniformly divided on the ordinate or y axis of the coordinates on which the u scale is plotted, with zero at the origin or intersection of the x and y axes. The $f_4(w)$ scale is uniformly divided on a line parallel to the y axis and one unit to the left in the second and third quadrants. The equation for this line is $x = -1$. Zero of the w scale is on the x axis.

The size of the $f_3(v)$ and $f_4(w)$ scales is identical and may be as large as the space allows. A satisfactory distance between the two scales may be determined by the available space and by noting from the table of values of u, x, and y the space taken by the location of the u scale on the coordinates. In this example the portion of the u scale shown is in the first quadrant, but it may lie in any quadrant; in fact, in this instance the u scale passes out to infinity and returns in the third quadrant for values higher than nine.

In Fig. 43, the same equation as in Fig. 42 is taken as the example. The formula

$$H = 0.0274V^2 + 0.0141LV^{1.83}$$

when divided through by $0.0274V^2$ and rearranged, becomes

$$\left(\frac{1}{0.0274V^2}\right)H + \left(\frac{-0.0141V^{1.83}}{0.0274V^2}\right)L = 1$$

$$x = \frac{\dfrac{0.0141V^{1.83}}{0.0274V^2}}{\dfrac{1}{0.0274V^2} - \dfrac{0.0141V^{1.83}}{0.0274V^2}} = \frac{0.0141V^{1.83}}{1 - 0.0141V^{1.83}}$$

$$y = \frac{0.0274V^2}{1 - 0.0141V^{1.83}}$$

The H scale corresponds to the $f_3(v)$ scale and the L scale corresponds to the $f_4(w)$ scale. The points on the V scale, corre-

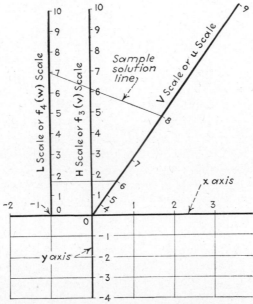

FIG. 43.—The curved scale can be plotted on graph paper from a table of values computed from standard formulas.

sponding to the u scale, are plotted from data given in the table shown at the top of page 62, which were computed from the above equations.

If the scales of $f_3(v)$ and $f_4(w)$ are to ascend in opposite directions, the type form of the equation is rewritten thus:

$$f_1(u)\, f_3(v) + [-f_2(u)][-f_4(w)] = 1$$

V	x	y
1	0.0143	0.0278
2	0.053	0.1154
3	0.1181	0.276
4	0.217	0.534
5	0.366	0.936
6	0.601	1.58
7	0.986	2.67
8	1.73	4.79
9	3.67	10.35

The equations for x and y are determined as for **Fig. 43** from the revised equation:

$$\left(\frac{1}{0.0274V^2}\right)H + \left(\frac{0.0141V^{1.83}}{0.0274V^2}\right)(-L) = 1$$

With this shift of signs, x and y become

$$x = \frac{-0.0141V^{1.83}}{1 + 0.0141V^{1.83}} \qquad y = \frac{0.0274V^2}{1 + 0.0141V^{1.83}}$$

In this instance the H scale corresponds to the $f_3(v)$ scale and the L scale corresponds to the $-f_4(w)$ scale.

In Fig. 44 are shown points plotted from data given in the following table which were computed from the above equations.

V	x	y
1	−0.0139	0.027
3	−0.0953	0.223
5	−0.211	0.540
7	−0.332	0.898
10	−0.488	1.403
15	−0.667	2.05
20	−0.772	2.50

Since these few points determine the scale line closely enough, additional and intermediate values of V may be located by using the H and L scales and the original equation. Thus, when $V = 8$ and $L = 5$,

$$H = 0.0274 \times 8^2 + 0.0141 \times 5 \times 8^{1.83}$$
$$= 1.7536 + 3.1684 = 4.92$$

Tabulated values of V may also be checked by this method.

Since L is negative in this instance, values of L are plotted in the third quadrant.   This usually makes a nomogram of inconvenient proportions.   Since it is desirable to use a method that

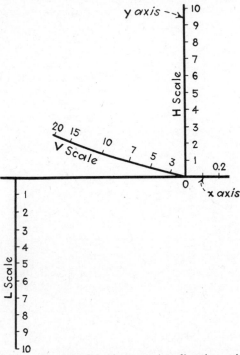

Fig. 44.—Parallel scales ascending in opposite directions with curved scale plotted in rectangular coordinates.

will confine the plotted curve between the parallel lines, means will be considered to bring the $f_3(v)$ and $f_4(w)$ scales opposite each other.

It can be proved in analytic geometry that curves may be plotted on axes that are not at right angles to each other just as readily as on "squared" paper without any change of method or theoretical considerations.   Since it is not relevant to the subject to go into this proof, it will be assumed that it is accepted. The use that is made of this fact is to raise the $f_4(w)$ scale as many units [either $f_3(v)$ or $f_4(w)$ units] as desired, assuming that the x axis still passes through the zeros of the two function scales.

Thus, in Fig. 45 the L scale of Fig. 44 has been raised 10 units. The oblique x axis is shown also in Fig. 45. It is confusing to plot in oblique coordinates and it is inconvenient to be required to draw graph paper to suit any angle that might be selected.

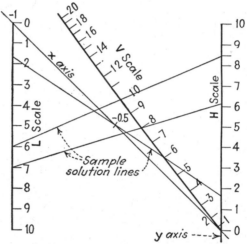

Fɪɢ. 45.—The curved V scale is plotted in oblique coordinates from calculated
values derived from the table for nomogram in Fig. 44.

It is possible to plot in imaginary oblique coordinates while actually plotting on rectangular coordinates by making an adjustment in the formula for y. The actual rectangular coordinates have their origin at zero of the H scale in Fig. 45. All values of x will be the same as for Fig. 44. An increment must be added to y values dependent upon the number of units, s, that zero of the $f_4(w)$ scale is raised. The new ordinate y' is determined by the formula

$$y' = y - sx \text{ (Appendix 10)}$$

The sign is minus because x values are negative. Using the same formulas for x and y as for Fig. 44 and assuming the L scale is raised 10 units, the curve would be plotted from the table shown on page 65, which was derived from the table used for Fig. 44.

The completed nomogram is shown in Fig. 45 and is identical with that produced graphically in Fig. 42. Comparing this form

V	x	y'
1	−0.0139	0.166 = 0.027 + 0.139
3	−0.0953	1.176
5	−0.211	2.65
7	−0.332	4.22
10	−0.488	6.28
15	−0.667	8.72
20	−0.772	10.22

with Figs. 43 and 44 for the same equation, it is obvious that the form of Figs. 42 and 45 is most satisfactory for this equation.

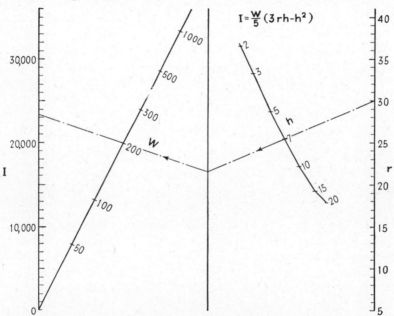

Fig. 46.—Moment of inertia of a spherical sector with reference to an axis through the radial center line.

However, it should not be assumed that this is true for every instance.

In case the ranges of $f_3(v)$ and $f_4(w)$ are widely different, it is desirable to have scales of the same length but with different-size units. In this instance the type equation is written

$$Rf_1(u)\left[\frac{f_3(v)}{R}\right] + f_2(u)\,f_4(w) = 1$$

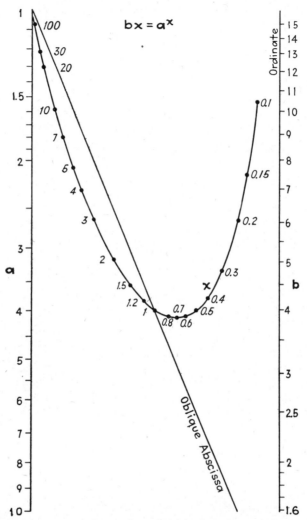

Fig. 47.—Two values of x are determined in the nomogram for $bx = a^x$.

when the $f_3(v)$ scale has R times the range of the $f_4(w)$ scale. From this equation

$$x = \frac{-f_2(u)}{f_5(u) + f_2(u)} \qquad y = \frac{1}{f_5(u) + f_2(u)}$$

where $f_5(u) = Rf_1(u)$.   A new function of v, $f_6(v)$, is equal to the old function $f_3(v)$ divided by R.   The size of the unit of y is the same as a unit of $f_6(v)$ and $f_4(w)$.

In the previously used condenser-tube formula, when the range of H is from 0 to 100 and that of L is from 0 to 10, the H scale

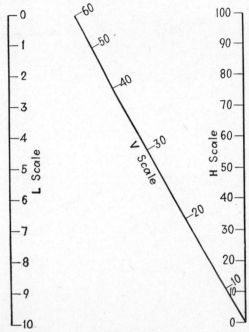

FIG. 48.—The range of the H scale is from 0 to 100 while the L scale has a range from 0 to 10.

has 10 times the range of the L scale.   Therefore $R = 10$.   The equation would be written

$$\left(\frac{10}{0.0274V^2}\right)\frac{H}{10} + \left(\frac{0.0141V^{1.83}}{0.0274V^2}\right)(-L) = 1$$

This variation will give the following equations for x and y:

$$x = \frac{-0.0141V^{1.83}}{10 + 0.0141V^{1.83}} \qquad y = \frac{0.0274V^2}{10 + 0.0141V^{1.83}}$$

$$f_6(v) = f(H) = \frac{H}{10} \qquad f_4(w) = f(L) = -L$$

The fact that the H scale will have 100 divisions and the L scale 10 divisions may raise the question whether the L scale is raised 10 or 100 units. The function of H, $H/10$, equals 10 when H equals 100. Zero of the function of L scale is opposite this value. Therefore the scale is raised 10 units.

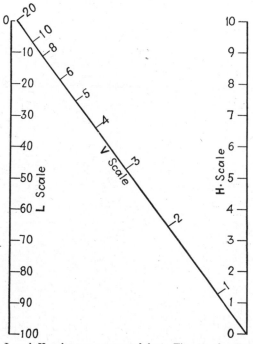

Fig. 49.—The L and H values are reversed from Fig. 48, the H scale having a range of 0 to 10 and the L scale 0 to 100.

In Fig. 48 are shown points plotted from data given in the following table which are computed from the above equations.

V	y	x	y'
10	0.250	−0.0871	1.121
20	0.819	−0.253	3.35
30	1.444	−0.414	5.58
40	1.992	−0.555	7.54
50	2.432	−0.645	8.88
60	2.79	−0.715	9.94

Assuming that the range of H is from 0 to 10 and that L is from 0 to 100, as in Fig. 49, the equation can be written

$$\left(\frac{1}{0.274V^2}\right)(10H) + \left(\frac{0.0141V^{1.83}}{0.0274V^2}\right)(-L) = 1$$

The equations for x and y would then be

$$x = \frac{-0.141V^{1.83}}{1 + 0.141V^{1.83}} \qquad y = \frac{0.274V^2}{1 + 0.141V^{1.83}}$$
$$f_6(v) = f(H) = 10H \qquad f_4(w) = f(L) = -L$$

In this instance the y axis is divided into 100 divisions [$f_6(v)$ varies from 0 to 100] for the function scale, and the L scale is raised 100 units to be opposite the H scale. In the transformation equation

$$y' = y - sx \qquad s = 100$$

In Fig. 49 are shown points plotted from data given in the following table, which were computed from the above equations.

V	y	x	y'
1	0.240	−0.124	12.60
2	0.730	−0.333	34.08
3	1.199	−0.513	52.5
4	1.578	−0.641	65.7
5	1.861	−0.728	74.7
6	2.08	−0.790	81.1
8	2.39	−0.864	88.8
10	2.60	−0.905	93.1
20	3.15	−0.972	100.3

Still other forms of the condenser-tube nomogram are shown in Figs. 55 and 56.

The nomogram for the equation relating radius, chord, and sagitta of an arc in Fig. 50 apparently has two values of h. The smaller value is the one normally used and the larger value is always greater than the radius. Normally only one leg of the h scale line would be drawn.

This nomogram is an example in which one of the parallel scales is not uniformly divided. The equation

$$R = \frac{c^2 + 4h^2}{8h}$$

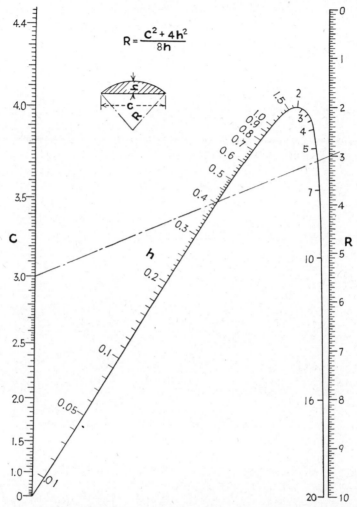

FIG. 50.—Nomogram for circular segment. Two values of h can be determined here but only one is the sagitta. The other is the diameter minus h.

is rewritten

$$R\left(\frac{2}{h}\right) + (-c^2)\left(\frac{1}{4h^2}\right) = 1$$

$$f_3(v) = R \qquad f_4(w) = f(c) = -c^2$$

$$x = \frac{\dfrac{-1}{4h^2}}{\dfrac{2}{h} + \dfrac{1}{4h^2}} \qquad y = \frac{1}{\dfrac{2}{h} + \dfrac{1}{4h^2}}$$

The location of the point 0.1 on the h scale relative to coordinates intersecting at zero on the R scale, assuming the c scale line is on the line represented by $x = -1$, is

$$x = \frac{-5}{9} \qquad y' = \frac{1}{45} + 10 \times \frac{5}{9} = \frac{251}{45} = 5.57$$

Other points can be determined similarly.

Oblique axes can be used also when the $f_3(v)$ and $f_4(w)$ scales ascend in the same direction and when the u scale line is not between these two scale lines. For example, when the above equation is nomographed with R and c scales ascending in the same direction in rectangular coordinates, the h scale line extends out almost perpendicularly along the x axis. With oblique axes the h scale line may make any angle with the vertical scales.

For this instance the equation is rewritten

$$R\left(\frac{2}{h}\right) + c^2\left(\frac{-1}{4h^2}\right) = 1$$

$$f_3(v) = R \qquad f_4(w) = f(c) = c^2$$

$$x = \frac{\dfrac{1}{4h^2}}{\dfrac{2}{h} - \dfrac{1}{4h^2}} \qquad y = \frac{1}{\dfrac{2}{h} - \dfrac{1}{4h^2}}$$

Assuming the $f(c)$ scale is dropped three units, y', which is used with oblique-type nomograms instead of y, equals $y + 3x$. The h scale, therefore, can be plotted by determining x and y' values for the desired values of h.

Before plotting this scale, however, let it be assumed that it is desirable to have the $f(c)$ scale of a different size than the R scale. Let the R scale unit be, for example, $\frac{5}{6}$ as large as a $f(c)$ unit. This can be handled in the equation by writing it as follows:

$$R\left(\frac{2}{h}\right) + \left(\frac{6}{5}c^2\right)\left(-\frac{5}{6} \cdot \frac{1}{4h^2}\right) = 1$$

Then

$$f_3(v) = R \qquad f_4(w) = f(c) = \frac{6c^2}{5}$$

$$x = \frac{\dfrac{5}{24h^2}}{\dfrac{2}{h} - \dfrac{5}{24h^2}} \qquad y' = \frac{1}{\dfrac{2}{h} - \dfrac{5}{24h^2}} + 3x$$

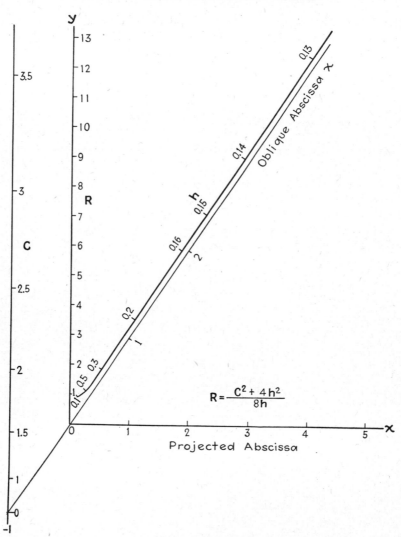

$$R = \frac{C^2 + 4h^2}{8h}$$

FIG. 51.—Figure 50 was distorted to make this chart.   The c scale was reversed in direction and oblique axes turned in the opposite direction.

Computations from these equations are tabulated below for several divisions on the h scale which are shown in Fig. 51.

h	x	y'
1	0.116	0.906
0.5	0.263	1.105
0.3	0.531	1.820
0.2	1.088	3.473
0.16	1.866	5.83
0.15	2.28	7.07
0.14	2.90	8.97
0.13	4.02	12.39

TYPE 19

Nomograms for $\dfrac{f_1(u)}{f_3(v)} + \dfrac{f_2(u)}{f_4(w)} = 1$

This form is essentially the same as Type 18, but if treated in the same manner would have reciprocal scales of the functions of v and w. It occasionally happens that only one of these is reciprocal. In this event a reciprocal scale cannot be avoided, but it is possible to choose which variable would be least objectionable as a reciprocal scale.

The graphical method of laying out a nomogram of the above type is illustrated in Fig. 52. Two straight lines intersecting at right angles are drawn. One line is uniformly divided with a scale of $f_3(v)$ and the other with a scale of $f_4(w)$ so that zero of both scales is at the intersection of the two lines. The size of each scale is independent of the other and may be as large as the space allows for the given limits.

To locate the u scale line, a value of $f_3(v)$ or $f_4(w)$ is selected and the original equation is solved for $f_4(w)$ or $f_3(v)$, respectively, for a set of values of u which are placed on the u scale. This process is repeated for another value of $f_3(v)$ or $f_4(w)$, using the same values of u. The intersections of lines corresponding to the same value of u will locate values of u on the u scale. The function scales are then replaced with scales of the variable.

As an example, the electrical capacity of a vertical wire relatively high above ground is determined by the formula

$$C = \frac{0.2416L}{\log_{10}\left(\dfrac{2L}{d}\right)}$$

C = capacity in micromicrofarads.
L = length in centimeters.
d = wire diameter in centimeters.

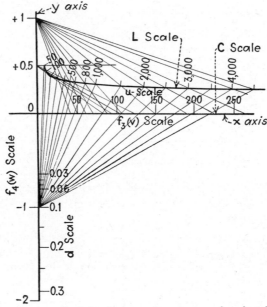

Fig. 52.—Graphical method for laying out nomogram for electrical capacity of a vertical wire relatively high above ground.

It may be written

$$\frac{\left(\dfrac{0.2416L}{\log 2L}\right)}{C} + \frac{\dfrac{1}{\log 2L}}{\dfrac{1}{\log d}} = 1$$

Therefore C corresponds to $f_3(v)$ and $\dfrac{1}{\log d}$ corresponds to $f_4(w)$.

A set of values of C can be determined for $f_4(w) = 1$ and $f_4(w) = -1$. These are tabulated below. For low values of L, C is determined for $f_4(w) = 0.5$.

L	$C_{0.5}$	C_1	C_{-1}
50	∞	. . . . .	6.04
100	80.3	. . . . .	7.32
200	80.3	. . . . .	13.41
300	93.2	. . . . .	19.17
400	101.4	. . . . .	24.76
500	120.8	. . . . .	30.2
600	. . . . .	69.7	35.5
800	. . . . .	87.7	46.0
1000	. . . . .	105.0	56.1
1500	. . . . .	146.3	81.0
2000	. . . . .	185.6	105.0
2500	. . . . .	223.9	128.5
3000	. . . . .	261	151.6
3500	. . . . .	297	174.5
4000	. . . . .	333	197.0
4500	. . . . .	368	219.5

THE PLOTTING METHOD

The plotting method is as simple as the graphical method. The $f_3(v)$ scale is uniformly divided on the x axis at the origin and the $f_4(w)$ scale is uniformly divided on the y axis with zero at the origin. The size of each scale is independent of the other and may be as large as the space allows for the given limits.

For the location and subdivision of the u scale, let

$$x = f_1(u) \qquad y = f_2(u)$$

A table is made of the values of x and y for each value of u which it is desired to show on the u scale line. The values are plotted on the coordinates formed by the $f_3(v)$ and $f_4(w)$ scale lines, using the scales selected for each. The function scales of v and w are then replaced with scales of the variables.

The foregoing example shown in Fig. 52 is used again here.

$$x = \frac{0.2416L}{\log 2L} \qquad y = \frac{1}{\log 2L}$$

The points are plotted in the nomogram in Fig. 53, from the data given in the above table which are computed from the above equations. The illustration shows how the nomogram should appear in completed form except for insufficient scale divisions.

L	x	y	x' (see Fig. 54)
50	6.04	0.5	−63.96
100	10.50	0.434	−50.25
300	26.1	0.360	−24.3
500	40.3	0.333	− 6.3
1000	73.2	0.303	+30.8
1500	104.2	0.288	63.9
2000	134.1	0.277	95.3
2500	163.3	0.270	125.5
3000	191.8	0.265	154.7
3500	220.0	0.260	183.6
4000	247.6	0.256	211.8
4500	275	0.253	239.6

By using the formula for x, it is a simple matter to fill in scale divisions on the L scale.

Oblique coordinates may be used, determined either graphically or by the plotting method. The relative positions of the v and w

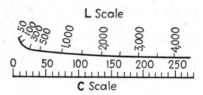

Fig. 53.—The u scale values are plotted on the coordinates formed by the $f_3(v)$ and $f_4(w)$ scale lines.

scales should be known before starting, since the w scale may be on the $+y$ axis, in which instance the y axis would swing in the other direction. In the example illustrated in Fig. 54, the $f_4(w)$ scale of Fig. 53 is swung so that $f_4(w) = 2$ is moved to the right

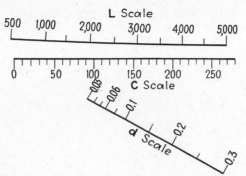

Fig. 54.—Oblique coordinates can be used for locating the *u* scale either graphically or by plotting.

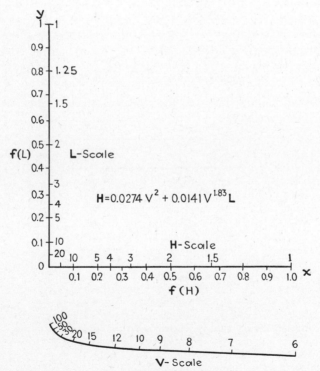

$$H = 0.0274\,V^2 + 0.0141\,V^{1.83}\,L$$

Fig. 55.—Not a very convenient manner of handling this equation, but it is one way of doing it.

280 units.   This means that x values in the above table must be decreased by $140y$ to give new x' values tabulated above.

Although the condenser-tube equation is not suited to this type of nomogram, it is possible to make a chart of this type that will solve the equation.   The equation

$$H = 0.0274V^2 + 0.0141LV^{1.83}$$

should be rewritten

$$\frac{\dfrac{1}{0.0274V^2}}{\dfrac{1}{H}} - \frac{\dfrac{0.0141V^{1.83}}{0.0274V^2}}{\dfrac{1}{L}} = 1$$

In this equation $1/H$ corresponds to $f_3(v)$ and $1/L$ corresponds to $f_4(w)$

$$x = \frac{1}{0.0274V^2} \qquad y = \frac{0.0141V^{1.83}}{0.0274V^2}$$

The V scale values shown in Fig. 55 were plotted from the table below.

V	x	y
5	1.46	-0.391
6	1.014	-0.379
7	0.745	-0.367
8	0.570	-0.361
9	0.451	-0.354
10	0.365	-0.348
12	0.261	-0.337
15	0.1622	-0.324
20	0.0913	-0.309
30	0.0406	-0.288
40	0.0228	-0.275
50	0.0146	-0.264
100	0.00365	-0.235

Oblique coordinates and use of only portions of the three scales make an entirely satisfactory nomogram of this equation as far as scales are concerned.   In Fig. 56 the L scale line of Fig. 55 is swung around to an acute angle with the H scale line.   The whole nomogram is turned another 90 deg. and enlarged for the shorter ranges of the variables, as shown.

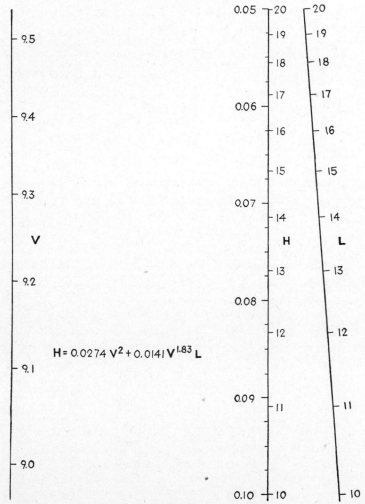

$$H = 0.0274 \, V^2 + 0.0141 \, V^{1.83} \, L$$

Fig. 56.—Portions of the scales of Fig. 55 are used here, and the L and H scale lines are turned to an acute angle. The *V* scale is plotted by the rules for oblique axes.

To accomplish this means only finding new values for *x*. The value 10 on the *L* scale in Fig. 55 is at $y = f(L) = 0.1$, and it is still to be considered at 0.1 unit perpendicularly from the *H* scale line in Fig. 56.   Since 0.1 on the $f(L)$ scale is moved 0.1 unit in the $+f(H)$ direction, x values in the above table must be reduced by corresponding y values before plotting the V scale.

$$x' = x + y$$

The plus sign is used because y values are negative.

V	x	y	x'
9.0	0.451	−0.354	0.097
9.1	0.441	−0.354	0.087
9.2	0.431	−0.353	0.078
9.3	0.425	−0.353	0.069
9.4	0.413	−0.352	0.061
9.5	0.404	−0.351	0.053

The above table was computed with a slide rule, which is not sufficiently accurate for plotting a chart of large proportions.

To show further versatility in making nomograms under Type 18, the several examples following have been devised.   Some are practical for use and others are curiosities.   The nomogram for the quadratic equation in Fig. 57 is a practical one that is well-known.   The horizontal p/q scale, however, is novel.   It permits use of p or q values above $+4$.

A variation in the form of the quadratic equation can be made to produce a circular scale line for the variable u, as in Fig. 58. The equation

$$cu^2 + u + d = 0$$

may be written

$$d\left(-\frac{1}{u}\right) + c(-u) = 1$$

Therefore

$$x = \frac{u}{-\dfrac{1}{u} - u} \qquad y = \frac{1}{-\dfrac{1}{u} - u}$$

$$x = \frac{-u^2}{u^2 + 1} \qquad y = \frac{-u}{u^2 + 1}$$

These equations will plot the desired values of u on a circular scale.   It is possible on any of the nomograms of this type to

plot the curved scale line by another means, namely, by deriving
the equation for the curve in terms of x and y only. The method
has been omitted here because, after plotting the scale line by

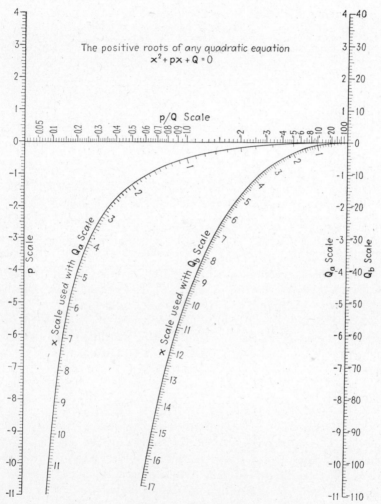

FIG. 57.—A nomogram of the quadratic equation.

such an equation, it is still necessary to subdivide a scale. It
is therefore desirable to use desired points on the scale to plot
the line.

From the two equations above, it is obvious that

$$x = uy \qquad u = \frac{x}{y}$$

Substituting this value of u in the equation for y,

$$y = \frac{\dfrac{-x}{y}}{\dfrac{x^2}{y^2} + 1} = \frac{-xy}{x^2 + y^2}$$

Therefore:

$$-y^2 = x^2 + x + (\tfrac{1}{2})^2 - (\tfrac{1}{2})^2$$
$$= (x + \tfrac{1}{2})^2 - (\tfrac{1}{2})^2$$

When the equation is written

$$(x + \tfrac{1}{2})^2 + y^2 = (\tfrac{1}{2})^2$$

it is recognized as the equation of a circle with its center at $x = -\tfrac{1}{2}$ and $y = 0$. The positive values of u are shown on the circular scale line in Fig. 58.

In the construction of curved-scale nomograms an infinite variety of shapes can be produced in the curved scale line by shifting the position of one of the parallel scale lines. In Fig. 59 is shown a nomogram having four h scales, each h scale being plotted by shifting the position of the working scale N (not shown). The nomogram represents the equation

$$V = \frac{2}{3}\sqrt{2g}\frac{\sqrt{h_1{}^3} - \sqrt{h_2{}^3}}{h_1 - h_2}$$

The equation is one in hydraulics and the manner of writing it in the type form was given under No. 7 on page 59. The four curves in Fig. 59 are drawn between the V and N scales, two values of h on the curved scale determining a value of V on the V scale. The cross sectioning assists in plotting the curves but is unnecessary in the completed nomogram.

The nomogram for determining the volume of a frustrum of a pyramid, useful in bin and hopper design, as shown in Fig. 60, is of interest, as four variables are involved. The principle is similar to that employed for constructing the nomogram shown in Fig. 59. The formula that the chart solves is

$$V = \frac{h}{3}(A_1 + A_2 + \sqrt{A_1A_2})$$

The variables A_1 and A_2, being the areas of the top and bottom of the pyramid, have identical scales superimposed upon each

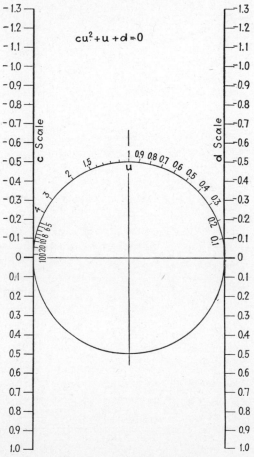

FIG. 58.—The nomogram for the quadratic equation can be made with one scale on a circular arc tangent to both parallel line scales.

other. The distance between the top and bottom, h, is scaled on the diagonal line, and the volume V of the pyramid is indicated on one of the vertical scale lines.

As an example of the use of the chart, a top area of one unit and a bottom area of six units are assumed. A line drawn

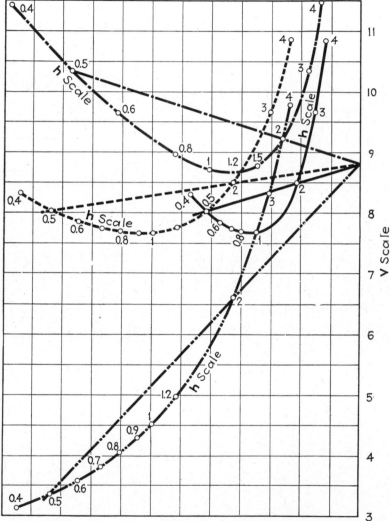

Fɪɢ. 59.—Showing the various shapes of the curved scale line developed by shifting the position of one of the straight-line scales.

through these two points on the A_1 and A_2 scale line intersects the vertical line at the right. A second line drawn from the determined point through the value $h = 4$ on the diagonal scale yields a value of 12.6 units for volume.

The formula can be changed to the form

$$\frac{3V}{h} = \frac{\sqrt{A_1{}^3} - \sqrt{A_2{}^3}}{\sqrt{A_1} - \sqrt{A_2}}$$

by multiplying the equation for volume by

$$\frac{\sqrt{A_1} - \sqrt{A_2}}{\sqrt{A_1} - \sqrt{A_2}}$$

This equation can also be written

$$\frac{3V}{h}\sqrt{A_1} - \sqrt{A_1{}^3} = \frac{3V}{h}\sqrt{A_2} - \sqrt{A_2{}^3}$$

Using the variable A for A_1 or A_2 and introducing N,

$$\frac{3V}{h}\sqrt{A} - \sqrt{A^3} = N$$

A nomographic type form is derived by dividing through the equation by $\sqrt{A^3}$:

$$\left(\frac{3V}{h}\right)\left(\frac{1}{A}\right) + N\left(\frac{-1}{\sqrt{A^3}}\right) = 1$$

In the accompanying chart, limits of 0 to 12 were selected for the ratio $3V/h$, which is handled as a single variable. It is a matter of trial and error to determine suitable limits of N and the position of the N scale line. As indicated in Fig. 59, the possibilities are without limit. A portion of the N scale line is shown with the chart in Fig. 60, but it has no function in the completed chart and may be eliminated along with the numbers on the ratio scale line and the graph lines.

The $3V/h$ scale line serves as the y axis, and a line drawn horizontally through zero on this line is the x axis. The N scale line is at $x = -1$, and the N scale ascends in a direction opposite to the $3V/h$ scale. The N scale has also been raised 10 units to

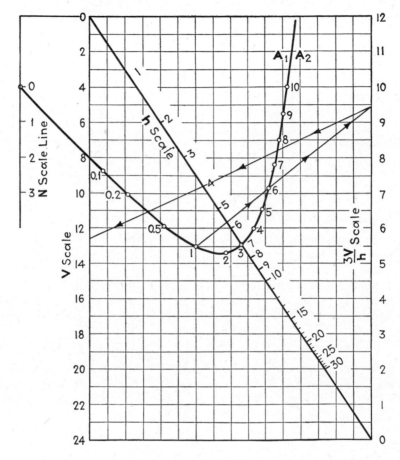

Nomogram for Determining the Volume of the Frustrum
of a Pyramid $V = \frac{h}{3}(A_1 + A_2 + \sqrt{A_1 A_2})$

Fig. 60.—Nomogram used in hopper or bin design for determining the volume
of the frustrum of a pyramid formed by the walls.

bring it opposite the other vertical scale.   The x and y coordinates
of the A_1 and A_2 scale were determined from the formulas

$$x = \frac{-1}{\sqrt{A} + 1} \qquad y = \frac{\sqrt{A^3}}{\sqrt{A} + 1}$$

These apply before raising the N scale 10 units.   If the N scale
is raised 10 units, y' is substituted for y ($y' = y + 10x$), while

x remains the same.

$$y' = \frac{\sqrt{A^3} + 10}{\sqrt{A} + 1}$$

A	x	y'	A	x	y'
0	-1	10.00	4	-0.333	6.00
0.1	-0.760	7.62	5	-0.309	6.55
0.2	-0.691	6.97	6	-0.290	7.16
0.3	-0.586	6.07	7	-0.274	7.81
1	-0.500	5.50	8	-0.261	8.52
2	-0.414	5.31	9	-0.250	9.25
3	-0.366	5.56	10	-0.240	10.00

The A_1 and A_2 scale was plotted from the above data. Computed in this manner, it is advantageous to lay out the chart on graph paper.

The second half of the equation, involving V and h, is simply a Z chart. It cannot be a logarithmic-scale chart because the $3V/h$ scale is uniformly divided for the other part of the chart.

ADVANCED METHOD APPLIED TO SIMPLE NOMOGRAMS

It was previously stated that methods applicable to equations in which there are two functions of one of the variables are applicable to simpler nomograms. It is interesting to see how this works out. As an example, the equation

$$D = 1.24\sqrt{\frac{L}{f}} + 0.088$$

one form of which was illustrated in Figs. 19 and 20, pages 30 and 31, will be used. First, the parallel-scale type will be considered. The equation may be written as Type 18:

$$\left(\frac{D - 0.088}{1.24}\right)^2 f + (-1)(L - 1) = 1$$

so that $\qquad f_1(u) = \left(\dfrac{D - 0.088}{1.24}\right)^2$ and $f_2(u) = -1$.

$$f_3(v) = f \qquad \text{and} \qquad f_4(w) = L - 1$$

By referring to the plotting method on page 60, it will be seen that

$$x = \cfrac{1}{\left(\cfrac{D - 0.088}{1.24}\right)^2 - 1} = \cfrac{1.538}{D^2 - 0.176D - 1.53} = y$$

The resulting nomogram is shown in Fig. 61. Although x and y values are numerically the same, the D scale is practically horizontal because of the great difference in the size of the x and y units. When $D = 1.6$, for example, $x = y = 2.06$.

If $f_2(u) = 1$ and $f_4(w) = -(L - 1)$,

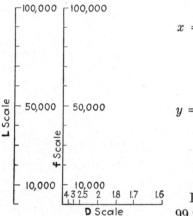

$$x = \cfrac{-1}{\left(\cfrac{D - 0.088}{1.24}\right)^2 + 1} =$$

$$\cfrac{-1.538}{D^2 - 0.176D + 1.545}$$

$$y = \cfrac{1}{\left(\cfrac{D - 0.088}{1.24}\right)^2 + 1} =$$

$$\cfrac{1.538}{D^2 - 0.176D + 1.545} = -x$$

Fig. 61.—Parallel-scale type of nomogram in this form is more complicated than the Z chart for the same formula shown in Fig. 21, page 32.

If the L scale is then raised 99,999 units, $y' = 100,000y$ and the resulting chart will be as shown in Fig. 21, page 32. The equation could also be written

$$2 \log \left(\frac{D - 0.088}{1.24}\right) = \log L - \log f$$

or

$$\frac{\log L}{f_1(D)} + \frac{-\log f}{f_1(D)} = 1$$

Then

$$x = \cfrac{\cfrac{-1}{f_1(D)}}{\cfrac{1}{f_1(D)} + \cfrac{1}{f_1(D)}} = -\frac{1}{2}$$

$$y = \log \left(\frac{D - 0.088}{1.24}\right)$$

Obviously, the resulting nomogram constructed by these equations would consist of equal-sized logarithmic scales of L and f ascending in opposite directions on parallel lines with the D scale, as defined by the equation for y above, on a third parallel line halfway between them.

Similarly the equation for bolt strength could be arranged for intersecting scales of L and f by writing it in the form of Type 19.

Then $f_1(u) = f_2(u) = \dfrac{1}{f_1(D)}$; $f_3(v) = \dfrac{1}{\log L}$; and $f_4(w) = \dfrac{-1}{\log f}$

$$x = \frac{1}{f_1(D)} \qquad y = \frac{1}{f_1(D)}$$

But the resulting nomogram would be unwieldy and impractical.

Just as it has been shown possible to construct all nomograms from a theory set up for the more complex types, it is also possible to build a theory around determinants which is applicable to all nomograms. The algebraic manipulation is cumbersome and voluminous by either method for the most common equations, so that for practical applications the labor involved in construction is rarely justified. Transformations of equations into determinate forms are frequently puzzle problems if they are workable at all. It has been stated that no test has been found which could show definitely if it is possible to reduce certain equations to the most general determinate form.

Some equations have been put into nomographic form without benefit of theory where two functions of two variables are in symmetrical relation. An example of this kind is the equation

$$w = uv + \sqrt{u^2 + 1} \ \sqrt{v^2 + 1}$$

It is far from obvious how this equation can be put into the type form for equations having two functions of two of the variables for construction of a nomogram having two curved and one straight-line scales:

$$f(w) = \frac{f_1(u)\,f_2(v) - f_2(u)\,f_1(v)}{f_1(u) - f_1(v)}$$

or

$$f(w) = \frac{f_1(u) - f_1(v)}{f_2(u) - f_2(u)}$$

Yet the nomogram in Fig. 62 solves the equation. Being con-

structed graphically, the first set of construction lines is drawn,
assuming $u = v$ and assuming the values of u and v to be on

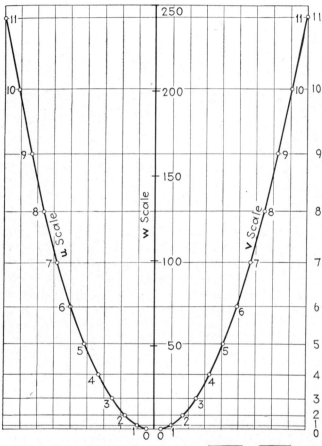

Fig. 62.—Nomogram of equation $w = uv + \sqrt{u^2 + L}\,\sqrt{v^2 + 1}$ after transformation to workable type form.

lines drawn horizontally through values of w on a uniform scale
as determined by the formula

$$w = 2u^2 + 1$$

The second set is assumed to pass through a constant value of
u or v, for example, $u = 10$, which is located as far from the w
scale as desired.   The equation would be

$$w = 10u + \sqrt{101}\sqrt{u^2 + 1}$$

The fault in the theory of construction is that there is no proof for any value other than 10. However, when a similar scale is made for v, the nomogram is found to be practicable for all values.

The method holds true also with the equation

$$Z = K \frac{A^3 \times B^3}{A + B}$$

both with a uniform scale of Z and with logarithmic scale, although the method is known to be impracticable in other similar equations.

At this point it may be recalled that the equation

$$V = \frac{2}{3}\sqrt{2g}\frac{\sqrt{h_1{}^3} - \sqrt{h_2{}^3}}{h_1 - h_2}$$

for which a nomogram is illustrated in Fig. 59, is in the abbreviated type form of a two-curve-scale nomogram. The equation for the curves of h_1 and h_2, however, will be found to be identical and therefore to lie in the same position, so that the resulting nomogram constructed by this method would be the same as in Fig. 59. If the signs between h_1 and h_2 had been plus, two curves would have been necessary.

Curve Nets

When there are more than three variables in an equation, they may be handled as in Figs. 16, 17, 24, 27, 60, and others, or by using a "curve net" or family of curves. The equation for the volume of a frustrum of a pyramid might be made in the form shown in Fig. 63 when a "curve net" is used. In this instance the result is not satisfactory because the range of h is limited for reasonable accuracy and because values of A less than unity are so close together that they are indistinguishable (see Appendix 11).

Figure 63 is simply eight nomograms in one, relating V, A_1, and A_2 with h held constant. Any straight line across the chart will indicate four values that will satisfy the equation, provided A_1 and A_2 are read on the same curve. Each of the eight nomograms is constructed by the method used for Fig. 60.

A nomogram of this type which is more satisfactory is shown in Fig. 64. There are five variables in the equation that is repre-

sented.   It gives not only volumes of liquid in horizontal cylindrical tanks with spheroidal ends for any depth of liquid but,
with a simple side calculation, the volumes in tanks of elliptical

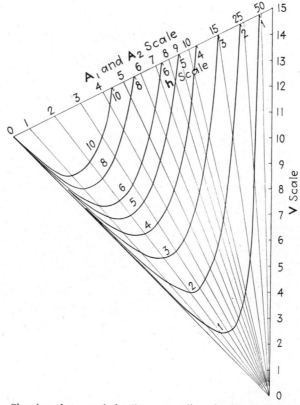

Fig. 63.—Showing the use of the "curve net" or family of curves in chart
construction.

cross section and with ellipsiodal ends.   Flat-end tanks are also
included.
   The equation is

$$\frac{4V}{d^2} = \frac{1728}{231} 4\pi t \left(\frac{h}{d}\right)^2 \left(1 - \frac{2h}{3d}\right)$$
$$+ L\left[\cos^{-1}\left(1 - \frac{2h}{d}\right) - 2\left(1 - \frac{2h}{d}\right)\sqrt{\frac{h}{d} - \left(\frac{h}{d}\right)^2}\,\right]$$

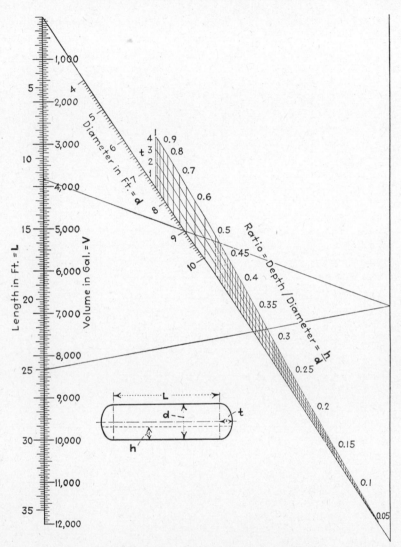

F<small>IG</small> 64.—Chart for determining volume of liquid at any depth in a horizontal cylindrical tank with spheroidal ends.

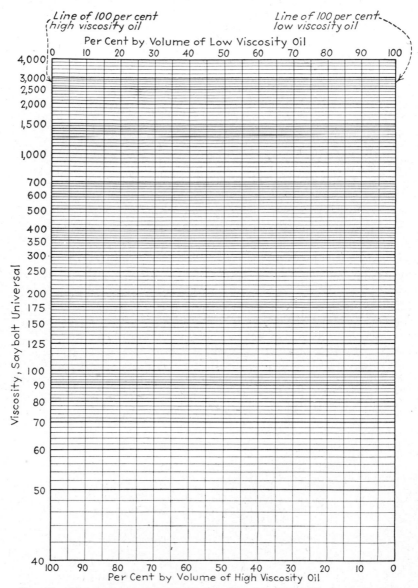

Fɪɢ. 65.—Nomogram used for predicting the viscosity of blends of oil of the same base when high- and low-viscosity oils are mixed.

V = volume of liquid in tank in gallons.

d = diameter in feet.

L = length in feet.

h = depth of liquid in feet.

t = additional length on the center line of the tank because of the spheriodal ends.

When computing ellipsiodal tanks, the square root of the product of the total tank depth and tank width is substituted for d.

Figure 65 is also a "curve net" type nomogram although it looks like ordinary graph paper at first glance. It solves the equation

$$\frac{100}{6.5\sqrt{V}} = \frac{P}{6.5\sqrt{v_1}} + \frac{100 - P}{6.5\sqrt{v_2}}$$

The formula gives the kinematic viscosity V of a blend of two oils from the same base of viscosity v_1 and v_2 at the same temperature of the blend when P is the percentage by volume of the higher viscosity component. Fundamentally it is an equation of the type

$$2f(V) = f(v_1) + f(v_2) \qquad \text{when} \qquad P = 50$$

Normally the $f(V)$ scale would be half the size of the $f(v_1)$ and $f(v_2)$ scales, but the figure 2 in the equation doubles its size. All functions being identical, the scales also are identical. Similar reasoning could be applied if the values of P were other than 50.

APPENDIX

1. To prove the method of locating the z scale by the construction method, it is necessary to show that the loci of the points of intersection of the lines joining corresponding x and y values will be a straight line parallel to the x and y scales, and also that the readings on the z scale will always represent the sum of any pair of connected points on the x and y scales.   Referring to Fig. 1, it is obvious that a series of lines will intersect at a single point when these two conditions are met:

a. When a series of straight lines are drawn across two parallel lines so that each intersection with one parallel line is a constant distance above the intersection with the preceding line.

b. When each intersection of the series in the same order on the second parallel line is always a constant distance below the intersection with the preceding line.

Because such a series of lines can be started in any random position, the intersections of all such series will be found to lie in a third straight line which is parallel with the first two vertical lines, providing the same constant distances on these lines are used.

The above principles are used in the simplest nomograms. When parallel lines have a sequence of numbers assigned to equal divisions, it is possible to add or subtract since every series of lines intersecting at a common point on the third parallel line represents a different sum or difference which can be indicated, as in Fig. 1, by a corresponding number.

2. To prove Eqs. (1) and (2) on page 2 for the formula method, the following relations hold for the similar triangles in Fig. 1:

$$\frac{g}{3m_x} = \frac{h}{3m_y}$$

Here g and h are the altitudes of the two triangles shown. Therefore:

$$\frac{g}{h} = \frac{m_x}{m_y} \qquad \frac{g}{h} + 1 = \frac{m_x}{m_y} + 1$$

97

from which

$$\frac{g+h}{h} = \frac{m_x + m_y}{m_y} = \frac{d}{h}$$

Solving this last equation for h gives Eq. (2) on page 2. Substituting for h, its value $g m_y / m_x$ gives Eq. (1).

3. As in the discussion of Fig. 2, the same principle holds true for the equation $ax + by = cz$, because the constants a, b, and c affect only the numbering system of the subdivided scales. If $ax = u$, $by = v$, and $cz = w$, the equation reverts back to the simple form, $u + v = w$. The length of a unit of y is b times as long as a unit of v. This is evident from the following considerations. Assume that $b = 3$; then, when $y = 5$, $v = 15$ and, when $y = 6$, $v = 18$. Therefore, there are three units of v in the same space as one unit of y, or, per unit, y is three times as long.

However, to locate the scale line for z which will apply to this particular equation, it is necessary to compute with lengths of the units of u, v, and w which are equal to the lengths of units of x, y, and z divided by a, b, and c, respectively. The variables u, v, and w are really simple functions of x, y, and z, and the equation could be treated as the more general function equation.

4. Just as for parallel-line nomograms, similar triangles can be used to prove the construction of the Z chart. In the similar triangles OAP and $O'BP$ shown in Fig. A1

$$\frac{OA}{OP} = \frac{O'B}{OO' - OP}$$

Letting $x = OA$, $y = O'B$, and $z = OP$, the equation may be written

$$\frac{y}{x} = \frac{k - z}{z}$$

This equation is in the same form as that shown in Fig. 22 and shows why the a scale is uniformly divided.

The double Z chart, however, has a simpler explanation than that for three variables. There are two sets of similar triangles in Fig. A1 having the following relations:

$$\frac{OA}{BO'} = \frac{OP}{PO'} = \frac{OC}{DO'}$$

Letting $x = OA$, $y = BO'$, $u = OC$, and $v = DO'$, the equation may be written

$$\frac{x}{y} = \frac{u}{v}$$

as illustrated by the scales in the nomogram.

The same reasoning applies in Fig. 27 as in Fig. *A*1 or in other nomograms in which the pairs of parallel scale lines make angles

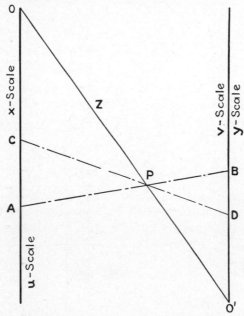

Fɪɢ. A1.—Similar triangles can be used to prove the construction of the Z chart.

other than 90 deg. with each other. If one more variable were included in Fig. 27, the diagonal line could then be used for one scale. Thus, assuming h is the product of two variables (xy), an equation could be written: $h/x = y$. The x scale would be opposite the S scale, the y scale would be on the diagonal, and the line on which the h scale is located would become an unscaled reference line.

5. Figure *A*2 shows why parallel lines may be used to solve a nomogram. At e the scales ascend in opposite directions. Any line ab crosses these scales, and the dotted line cO is drawn parallel to it through zero of one of the scales. It is immediately obvious

that any other parallel line passes through figures giving the same sum.   At *g* the scales ascend in the same direction and by similar reasoning the lines parallel to any random line *ab* produce constant differences.

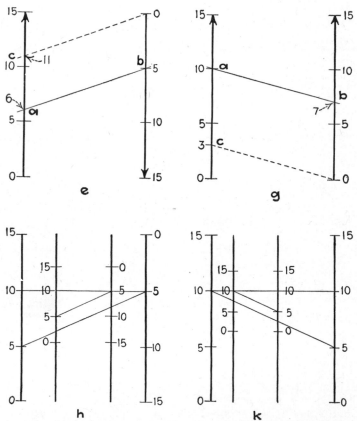

Fig. A2.—The principles of the use of parallel solution lines.

To transfer constant sums and differences to a second pair of scales, a second condition is imposed, namely, in changing from one constant sum or difference to another, the angle between the two different solution lines in each case must be the same.   This is illustrated in *h* and *k*.   Because the second pair of lines is closer together than the first pair and the solution lines make the same angle, a smaller scale is required for the lines that are closer together. Therefore, in the triangles formed

$$\frac{5m_1}{d_1} = \frac{5m_2}{d_2}$$

6. The application of parallel solution lines to the Z chart is further explained by reference to Fig. $A3$, in which the lines CD,

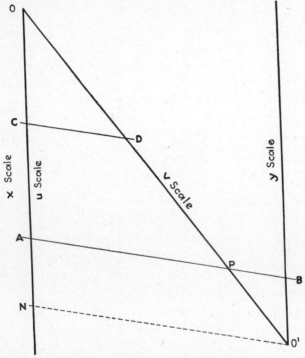

FIG. A3.—Similar triangles constructed with parallel solution lines can be used to prove the construction of the Z chart.

AB, and NO' are parallel. It is evident from similar triangles that

$$\frac{OA + O'B}{OO'} = \frac{OC}{OD}$$

since $O'B = AN$.

If $x = OA$, $y = O'B$, $u = OC$, $v = OD$, and OO' is a constant k, the equation becomes

$$\frac{x + y}{k} = \frac{u}{v}$$

By multiplying both u and v by any constant, the equality is unchanged so that the scales may be made to any size independent of the x and y scales.

The constant k has been combined with v in the procedure as if the equation were written

$$x + y = \frac{u}{\dfrac{v}{k}}$$

But since k is included in the proportion with x and y, k is measured in the same units as x and y and may be interpreted as the number of $f(x)$ or $f(y)$ units in the length of the diagonal. The length of the unit, v/k, would be the same as the unit of u. Therefore

$$m_v = km_u$$

The same, of course, applies to units of $f(v)/k$ and $f(u)$, so that

$$n_v = kn_u$$

7. The nomogram of Type 15 is of a more special character than other types that have been treated heretofore. Figure 36 shows why the equation can be solved graphically.

In the similar triangles xcy and xab

$$\frac{xc}{xa} = \frac{cy}{ab}$$

The lines ay and ab are parallel to uO and vO, respectively. The line uv was drawn parallel to xy. In the similar triangles aby and uvO

$$\frac{ay}{ab} = \frac{uO}{vO}$$

Since $cy = ay$,

$$\frac{cy}{ab} = \frac{uO}{vO}$$

Therefore

$$\frac{xc}{sa} = \frac{uO}{vO}$$

Since $yO = cO = aO$,

$$\frac{xO + yO}{xO - yO} = \frac{uO}{vO}$$

If $xO = x$, $yO = y$, $uO = u$, and $vO = v$,

$$\frac{x + y}{x - y} = \frac{u}{v}$$

If u and v are multiplied by the same constant, the equality is unaffected and therefore the size of the u and v scales is independent of the x and y scales.

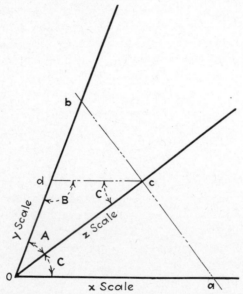

Fig. A4.—Relations of equation $Oa/Ob = dc/db = dc/(Ob - Od)$ shown by similar triangles. The law of sines can also be applied.

The procedure for this type of nomogram has been described for the instance where the solution lines are parallel, but it is obvious that, by swinging the u and v scale lines in Fig. 36 clockwise 90 deg., no change need be made in the development except that the solution lines are perpendicular to each other instead of being parallel.

8. The relationship of angular solution lines to given scales is shown in Fig. *A*4. The following relations are derived from similar triangles as illustrated by the equations

$$\frac{Oa}{Ob} = \frac{dc}{db} = \frac{dc}{Ob - od}$$

Applying the law of sines to the triangle Odc,

$$\frac{dc}{\sin A} = \frac{Oc}{\sin B} = \frac{Od}{\sin C}$$

From this equation, expressions for dc and Od can be obtained in terms of Oc:

$$dc = \frac{\sin A}{\sin B}Oc = K_1 Oc \qquad Od = \frac{\sin C}{\sin B}Oc = K_2 Oc$$

where K is a constant. Letting $x = Oa$, $y = Ob$, and $z = Oc$, the original equation may be written

$$\frac{x}{y} = \frac{K_1 z}{y - K_2 z}$$

Clearing fractions,

$$xy - xK_2 z = yK_1 z$$

Dividing through by xyz and rearranging,

$$\frac{K_1}{x} + \frac{K_2}{y} = \frac{1}{z}$$

It will be seen that any straight line across properly drawn scales of x, y, and z will solve this type of equation.

The procedure as given above for constructing the nomogram in Fig. $A4$ includes an arbitrary choice of values for K_1 and K_2 in the determination of the sizes of the $f_1(x)$ and $f_2(y)$ scales. It would be possible, knowing the ratio of K_1 and K_2, to compute the position of the $f_3(z)$ scale line.

$$\frac{K_1}{K_2} = \frac{dc}{Od}$$

In Fig. $A4$, therefore, with $K_1/K_2 = \frac{2}{3}$ approximately, it is also the ratio of dc to Od.

9. The theory of the construction of nomograms for equations containing one function of two variables and two functions of the third variable and, in fact, for any of the parallel-line nomograms considered up to this point, is derived from the equation of a straight line in rectangular coordinates. One form of this

equation is

$$\frac{y - y_1}{x - x_1} = \frac{y_1 - y_2}{x_1 - x_2}$$

In Fig. $A5$ a point corresponding to x, y is on the curve at the right. The point corresponding to x_1, y_1 is at v and that corre-

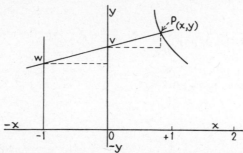

Fig. A5.—The equation of a straight line intersecting any three lines, one of which is curved, forms the basis for writing an equation for the curved line on which the scale for u in the equation $f_1(u)f_3(v) + f_2(u)f_4(w) = 1$ is placed.

sponding to x_2, y_2 is at w. The equation then can be written

$$\frac{y - v}{x - 0} = \frac{v - w}{0 + 1}$$

Solving for y,

$$y = v + vx - wx$$

or

$$y = v(x + 1) - wx$$

Dividing through by y,

$$1 = \frac{x + 1}{y}v - \frac{x}{y}w$$

or

$$\left(\frac{x + 1}{y}\right)v + \left(\frac{-x}{y}\right)w = 1$$

Since v and w represent values on the y axis and the line $x = -1$, respectively, and the two functions of x,y represent values on the curve, an equation that is written in the form

$$f_1(u)f_3(v) + f_2(u)f_4(w) = 1$$

can be solved by a straight line crossing scales of $f_3(v)$ and $f_4(w)$

on the y axis and the line $x = -1$, respectively, and a curve
plotted from values of x and y determined from the relations

$$\frac{x+1}{y} = f_1(u) \qquad -\frac{x}{y} = f_2(u)$$

$$\frac{1}{y} + \frac{x}{y} = f_1(u) \qquad \frac{1}{y} = f_1(u) + f_2(u)$$

$$y = \frac{1}{f_1(u) + f_2(u)}$$

$$x = -yf_2(u) = \frac{-f_2(u)}{f_1(u) + f_2(u)}$$

Similar equations can be worked out for any other positions
of the scales of $f_3(v)$ and $f_4(w)$ such as the y axis and $x = +1$, or

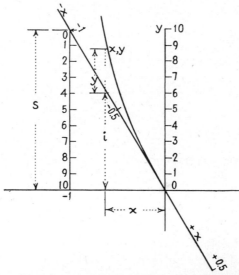

Fɪɢ. A6.—Showing the method of plotting oblique axes on rectangular coordinates whereby similar triangles are used for solution of the formula.

$x = -1$ and $x = +1$. It is sometimes possible with these
alternatives to simplify the computations.

A check on the location of the u scale is afforded by an inspec-
tion of the equation for x. With signs the same as above, it is
obvious that no value of x can be greater than unity and all
values lie between 0 and -1. Therefore, it is possible to visual-
ize the positions when the plotting method is used, before drawing
any line.

10. Plotting in oblique axes on rectangular coordinates is demonstrated in Fig. $A6$. By similar triangles it is obvious that

$$\frac{s}{1} = \frac{i}{x}$$

Therefore

$$i = sx \qquad y' = y + sx = y - s(-x)$$

11. When scales are placed on intersecting lines such as the abscissa and ordinate in Fig. A7, the general equation for a straight line through any point, P, may be written

$$\frac{y_1 - y}{x_1 - x} = \frac{y - y_2}{x - x_2}$$

The point (x_1, y_1) is at w and the point (x_2, y_2) is at v. The relation is obvious from the theorem of similar triangles. Then

$$\frac{w - y}{0 - x} = \frac{y - 0}{x - v}$$

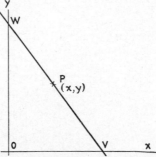

Fig. A7.—When scales are placed on intersecting lines Oy and Ox, the equation of a straight line passing through point P can be developed.

and by clearing fractions, dividing by vw, and rearranging, the equation becomes

$$\frac{x}{v} + \frac{y}{w} = 1$$

In this equation, v and w represent any points on the x and y axes and x and y the coordinates of points on a curved scale of u. An equation of the form

$$\frac{f_1(u)}{f_3(v)} + \frac{f_2(u)}{f_4(w)} = 1$$

can be applied directly to the construction of a nomogram on intersecting axes by letting $x = f_1(u)$, $y = f_2(u)$, and placing uniform scales of $f_3(v)$ and $f_4(w)$ on the x and y axes, respectively.

12. The "curve net" provides a means for solving a four-variable equation with a single line drawn across the chart. Where the labor and computation is great in laying out a curve

net, the object of making the nomogram is sometimes defeated because the nomogram is made to be a time saver where repeated computations of the same kind must be made.

In a three-variable equation the work corresponds to plotting curves in rectangular coordinates. However, it is frequently possible in plotting to straighten out a family of curves by using

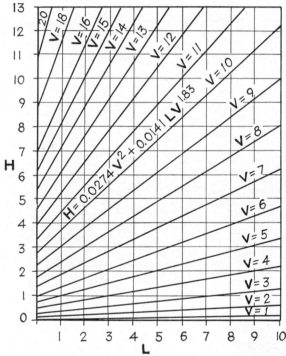

Fig. A8.—The slope-intercept form of the equation of a straight line is adapted to the equation for condenser tube friction loss to construct this chart.

special scales on the x and y axis or on both. A good example of this type of chart is the viscosity-temperature chart of the American Society for Testing Materials. On this chart it is possible to plot the viscosity of any lubricating oil as a straight line. The temperature scale of this chart is uniformly divided but the viscosity scale has been adjusted so that the relation is shown as a straight line. While this chart is not used in the same manner as those which are described in the following paragraph, it illustrates the principle.

The formidable-appearing condenser-tube equation can be plotted as a family of straight lines without special scales provided the proper variables are chosen for abscissa and ordinate.

To prepare this type of chart, the equation must be written to correspond to the slope-intercept form of the equation for a straight line:

$$y = mx + b$$

The equation

$$H = 0.0274V^2 + 0.0141LV^{1.83}$$

can be written in this form if V is assumed to be a constant. Then

$$H = K_1 + K_2L = K_2L + K_1$$

Therefore every value of V may be shown on coordinate axes as a sloping line, any point of which indicates by its position the values of H and L which satisfy the equation.

The following table was used to plot two points on each of the lines in Fig. $A8$.

V	L	H	B
1	10	0.168	0.0274
2	10	0.611	0.1096
3	10	1.300	0.2466
4	10	2.221	0.4383
5	10	3.366	0.685
6	10	4.727	0.986
7	10	6.30	1.342
8	10	8.09	1.753
9	10	10.08	2.220
10	10	12.27	2.740
11	6	10.12	3.315
12	5	10.59	3.945
13	4	10.80	4.63
14	3	10.67	5.37
15	2	10.16	6.16
16	2	11.54	7.015
18	1	11.67	8.88
20	1	14.36	10.97

If the variable V is on either of the coordinate axes, there is no way to straighten plotted curves of H or L.

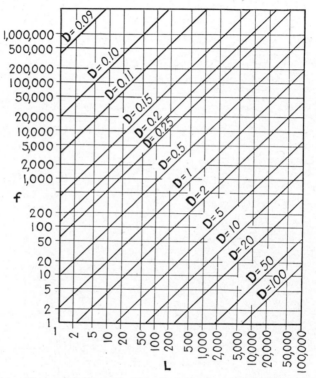

Fig. A9.—The straight-line equation can be used with logarithmic scales.

In the bolt-strength equation, any of the variables may be used on the axes. In Fig. $A9$ the equation

$$D = 1.24\sqrt{\frac{L}{f}} + 0.088$$

is plotted with logarithmic scales of L and f on the axes. The equation is rewritten

$$\log f = \log L - 2 \log \left(\frac{D - 0.088}{1.24}\right)$$

which corresponds to the slope-intercept form when D is constant. With equal-size scales of L and f, the slope, $m = 1$, is a constant 45 deg. for all values of D. All that need be computed is the *y* axis intercept for desired values of *D*. A few are tabulated below.

D	b[f(D)]	D	b	D	b	D	b
0.09	5.58	0.15	2.60	0.5	0.957	5	−1.20
0.10	4.03	0.20	2.09	1	0.267	10	−1.81
0.11	3.50	0.25	1.77	2	−0.376	20	−2.41
						50	−3.21

In Fig. *A*10 the special *D* scale is used on the *y* axis, and the logarithmic scale of *f* is plotted. The *L* scale is the same as in

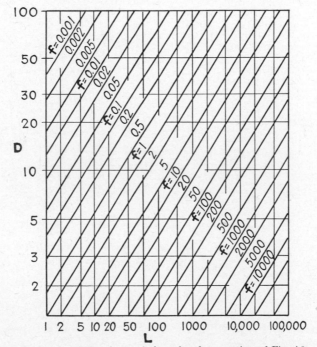

FIG. A10.—Another form of chart for the equation of Fig. A9.

Fig. *A*9. In either of these charts a single point solves the equation instead of a straight line across the chart.

There are still other possibilities with this type of equation. Uniformly divided scales can be used for *L* and *f*, for example. The equation may be written

$$L = \left(\frac{D - 0.088}{1.24}\right)^2 f + 0$$

The function of D may correspond to m and zero corresponds to b in the slope-intercept equation for a straight line:

$$y = mx + b$$

Therefore all D lines pass through the origin. Another point on each line may be computed. Lines in Fig. $A11$ were plotted from the data shown in the table at the top of page 113.

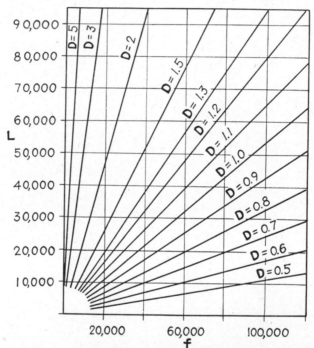

Fɪɢ. A11.—When uniform scales of L and f are used, the D lines converge at the origin.

Similarly the chart could be constructed with f corresponding to m. In this instance a special scale of D would be placed upon the x axis. Such a chart is shown in Fig. $A12$. No computations were necessary here to locate the f lines since the value of f is the slope of the line. Referring back to Fig. $A8$, there is found to be both a varying slope and intercept on account of the two

D	f(D)	f	L
0.5	0.1102	100,000	11,000
0.6	0.170	100,000	17,000
0.7	0.2435	100,000	24,350
0.8	0.329	100,000	32,900
0.9	0.4275	100,000	42,750
1.0	0.540	100,000	54,000
1.1	0.665	100,000	66,500
1.2	0.802	100,000	80,200
1.3	0.953	100,000	95,300
1.5	1.293	100,000	129,300
2.0	2.375	40,000	95,000
3.0	5.5	20,000	110,000
5.0	15.65	8,000	125,200

functions of V in the equation used. In Figs. $A9$ to $A12$ a choice is made between a constant slope and a constant intercept.

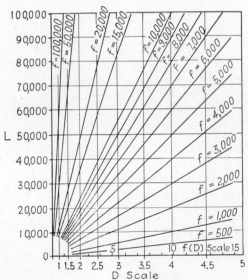

Fig. A12.—A special scale of D on the abscissa is necessary when D and f of Fig. A11 are interchanged.

In Fig. $A13$ is a chart for the volume of a frustrum of a pyramid, with the same formula as used for Fig. 60 and the same sample solution. In this instance no ordinate is used in the upper half of the chart. Every point, however, lies between two sets of lines which intersect each other. Four variables are handled in Fig. A13 by dividing the chart into two parts which are plotted on a common abscissa.

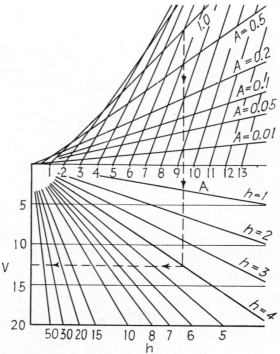

FIG. A13.—A combination chart using the principle of the equation of a straight line in both parts.

Obviously a great confusion of lines would result if all the lines of Figs. A8 to A13 were placed as close together as division lines are normally placed on nomographic scale lines. These charts, therefore, cannot in the same space give the accuracy of nomograms.